# SRA Imagine It!

# Lesson
# Assessment
# Book 1

## Annotated Teacher's Edition

**Level 4**

**SRA**

A Division of The **McGraw-Hill** Companies

P9-APL-395

SRAonline.com

Copyright © 2008 SRA/McGraw-Hill.

All rights reserved. No part of this publication may be
reproduced or distributed in any form or by any means,
or stored in a database or retrieval system, without the
prior written consent of The McGraw-Hill Companies, Inc.,
including, but not limited to, network storage or
transmission, or broadcast for distance learning.

Permission is granted to reproduce the printed material
contained on pages with a permission-to-reproduce copyright
line on the condition that such material be reproduced only
for classroom use; be provided to students, teachers, or
families without charge; and be used solely in conjunction
with *Imagine It!*, an Open Court Curriculum.

Printed in the United States of America.

Send all inquiries to this address:
SRA/McGraw-Hill
4400 Easton Commons
Columbus, OH 43219-6188

ISBN: 978-0-07-613099-3
MHID: 0-07-613099-1

1 2 3 4 5 6 7 8 9   MAZ   13 12 11 10 09 08 07

The *McGraw·Hill* Companies

# Table of Contents

# *Imagine It!* Lesson Assessment Books

*Lesson Assessment Book 1* and *Lesson Assessment Book 2* are an integral part of a complete assessment program that aligns with the instruction in *Imagine It! Lesson Assessment Book 1* covers material from Units 1–3. *Lesson Assessment Book 2* covers material from Units 4–6. The skills featured in lesson assessments are tied to reading success and reflect both state and national standards.

*Lesson Assessment Book 1* and *Lesson Assessment Book 2* offer the opportunity for summative and formative assessment. As students complete each lesson, they will be assessed on their understanding of the instructional content and the literature in each lesson. The results of the assessments will then be used to inform subsequent instruction. How students score on the assessments offers a picture of current student achievement status while also guiding you toward appropriate instructional decisions.

Each lesson assessment offers you the ability to gauge students' understanding of and growth in the following areas:

- Vocabulary
- Comprehension
- Grammar, Usage, and Mechanics
- Oral Fluency
- Writing

## Lesson Assessments

The lesson assessments consist of the following:

| Lesson Area | Format | Scope | Scoring |
|---|---|---|---|
| **Vocabulary** | Multiple Choice | Selection Vocabulary and Word Structure elements | 10 points (5 questions x 2 point) |
| **Comprehension** | Multiple Choice | Comprehension Skills | 5 points (5 questions x 1 point) |
| | Short Answer | Comprehension Skills | 10 points (5 questions x 2 points) |
| | Linking to the Concepts (Short Answer) | General comprehension related to a selection | 4 points (0-4 rubrics) |
| | Personal Response (Short Answer) | General comprehension related to a selection | 3 points (0-3 rubrics) |
| | Analyzing the Selection (Extended Response) | Understanding and development of ideas about selections and the unit theme | 8 points (0-8 rubrics) |
| **Grammar, Usage, and Mechanics** | Multiple Choice | Grammar, Usage, and Mechanics skills practiced in the lesson | 10 points (5 questions x 2 point) |
| **Oral Fluency** | Teacher-Directed Student Performance | Oral fluency development from lesson to lesson | Accuracy Rate on 100-point scale |

Students will be graded on their understanding of the vocabulary, word structure, comprehension, and grammar, usage, and mechanics skills taught in the lesson on a 50-point scale. A score of 80% (or 40 points out of 50) or higher on each lesson assessment is expected. Students may look back at the selection to answer the assessment questions. Students who consistently fall below 80% should be monitored for possible intervention. Students who are consistent low-performers in one or more aspects of the lesson assessment should be offered more practice in this lesson area during Workshop.

The Oral Fluency Assessments are scored separately. These assessments offer further data on student abilities. Student performance on oral fluency assessments is often a reliable predictor of student growth and understanding in other lesson areas. Students with consistently low accuracy rates and below-level words per minute numbers should be provided extra fluency practice during Workshop.

## End of Unit Writing Prompt

Over the course of the year, students will encounter six writing prompts, two each in the narrative, expository, and persuasive genres. These prompts reflect students' prior knowledge and experience with writing to a specific genre. Each prompt consists of a writing situation, a specific audience, directions for writing, and a checklist students can reference to ensure they receive the best score possible. Rubrics for scoring student work follow each prompt in this book. These rubrics pertain to genre, writing traits, and conventions. Students will be graded on a 20-point scale based on the rubrics—four points multiplied by five key writing features.

A score of 75% (or 15 points out of 20) or higher on each writing prompt is expected. Students can respond to the prompts in their student workbooks.

## Scores and Records

The opening page of each lesson assessment includes a place for students to write their names and the date, and for you to list their scores.

The Oral Fluency Assessment includes a box in which to write the accuracy rate.

The writing prompt includes a place for students to write their names and the date, and for you to list their scores.

Students' scores in the assessment can be registered in the Oral Fluency Scores, Class Assessment Record, and Student Assessment Record pages.

# Lesson Assessment Sections

Students may look back at the selection to answer the assessment questions.

## *Vocabulary*

Each vocabulary assessment is comprised of five multiple-choice questions worth two points each. Four of the questions feature selection vocabulary words from the lesson students have just completed. The remaining question in the assessment pertains to a word structure element from that lesson. The format of this question varies based on the word structure feature that is being assessed.

## *Comprehension: Multiple Choice*

Each comprehension assessment begins with five multiple-choice questions worth one point each. The items reflect the comprehension skills students have been taught specifically in that lesson and skills students have been previously taught.

# Comprehension: Short Answer

Next, students answer five short-answer questions worth two points each. These questions also reflect comprehension skills specific to the lesson and to students' prior knowledge and understanding of comprehension skills. Well-crafted and concise responses that answer the question fully should be awarded two points. Answers that partially address the question or are confusing and incomplete should be awarded a point, at your discretion. Answers that do not attempt to address the question or provide incorrect information should receive zero points.

Please note the "Possible answers below" following the directions in this Teacher's Edition. This serves as a reminder that students do not have to provide the exact answer shown, and that in some cases more than one answer is possible. For example, questions that ask for "one reason" or "one example" of something might be answered by a reason or example not specified in this Teacher's Edition.

# Comprehension: Linking to the Concepts

In this section, students craft a response to a question related to the selection they have just read. These questions do not focus on a particular comprehension skill; rather, they assess general comprehension of a selection by focusing on a key element in a selection which students should be comfortable identifying and writing to or about. These questions are worth four points each. Use the following criteria to judge student responses. To fully answer the question or prompt, student answers should be approximately forty to sixty words.

## Score: 4

The student understands the question and responds using information from the selection. The response is correct, reflects a thorough comprehension of the selection, and is an acceptably complete answer to the question. The organization of the response is meaningful, it is written smoothly, and sentences flow together. The response focuses on the topic. If multiple paragraphs are written, they are linked to one another with effective transitions. The response reads easily and demonstrates a sense of audience. It has correct spelling, grammar, usage, and mechanics, and it is written neatly and legibly.

## Score: 3

The student understands the question and responds using information from the selection. The response may reflect comprehension of the selection and is a somewhat complete answer to the question. The organization of the response is meaningful, it is written smoothly, and sentences flow together. The response focuses on the topic. If multiple paragraphs are written, they are linked to one another with effective transitions. The response reads easily and demonstrates a sense of audience. It has occasional errors in spelling, grammar, usage, and mechanics, and it is mostly written neatly and legibly.

## Score: 2

The student has partial understanding of the question. The response may reflect limited comprehension of the selection and is an incomplete answer to the question. The organization of the response is weak, it is written carelessly, and sentences are somewhat disorganized. The response includes extraneous information. If multiple paragraphs are written, they are linked to one another ineffectively. The response requires some effort to read easily and demonstrates a poor sense of audience. It has occasional errors in spelling, grammar, usage, and mechanics, and it is written somewhat neatly and legibly.

## Score: 1

The student has minimal understanding of the question. The response may reflect poor comprehension of the selection and is a barely acceptable answer to the question. The organization of the response is imprecise, it is written erratically, and sentences may be disjointed. The response is poorly focused. If multiple paragraphs are written, they are linked to one another inconsistently. The response is difficult to follow and may cause the reader to struggle. It has frequent errors in spelling, grammar, usage, and mechanics, and it is written with borderline neatness and legibility.

### Score: 0

The student fails to compose a response. If a response is attempted, it is inaccurate, meaningless, or irrelevant. The response may be written so poorly that it is neither legible nor understandable.

The following is an example of a response that would receive a score of "3" if it were mostly written neatly and legibly. The student shows an understanding of the question and relates information pertaining to the selection. The answer is organized, and the sections of the response relate to one another. However, the response spends more effort than needed describing *what* compost is, and the errors in spelling and grammar prevent it from being an exemplary response.

### SAMPLE

***Linking to the Concepts*** *Why do some people have compost piles?*

> *A compost pile uses rot to make good soil. People put garbige and things like leaves or grass in a compost pile. After a while the stuff rots and it turns into a kind of dirt that is good for a garden. These people probably have gardens.*

## Comprehension: Personal Response

In this section, students are asked to craft a personal response related to an idea or thematic issue raised by the selection they have just read. This section judges students' level of comprehension by assessing their ability to connect what they have just read to a personal level.

These questions are worth three points each. Use the following criteria to judge student responses. To fully answer the question or prompt, student answers should be approximately forty to sixty words.

### Score: 3

The student understands the question and responds suitably using a personal experience, opinion, prior knowledge, or plausible conjecture. The response reflects a thorough comprehension of the selection and is an acceptably complete answer to the question. The organization of the response is meaningful, it is written smoothly, and sentences flow together. The response focuses on the topic. If multiple paragraphs are written, they are linked to one another with effective transitions. The response reads easily and demonstrates a sense of audience. It has correct spelling, grammar, usage, and mechanics, and it is written neatly and legibly.

### Score: 2

The student understands the question and responds using a personal experience, opinion, prior knowledge, or plausible conjecture. The response may reflect partial comprehension of the selection and is a somewhat complete answer to the question. The organization of the response is imprecise, it is written erratically, and sentences may be somewhat disjointed. The response is not clearly focused. If multiple paragraphs are written, they are linked to one another ineffectively. The response is difficult to follow and demonstrates little awareness of the reader. It has a moderate number of errors in spelling, grammar, usage, and mechanics, and it is mostly written neatly and legibly.

### Score: 1

The student has minimal understanding of the question and responds using a personal experience, opinion, prior knowledge, or plausible conjecture. The response may reflect poor comprehension of the selection and is a barely acceptable answer to the question. The organization of the response is imprecise, it is written erratically, and sentences may be disjointed. The response is poorly focused. If multiple paragraphs are written, they are linked to one another inconsistently. The response is difficult to follow and may cause the reader to struggle. It has frequent errors in spelling, grammar, usage, and mechanics, and it is written with borderline neatness and legibility.

### Score: 0

The student fails to compose a response. If a response is attempted, it is inaccurate, meaningless, or irrelevant. The response may be written so poorly that it is neither legible nor understandable.

The following is an example of a response that would receive a score of "2" if it were mostly written neatly and legibly. The student shows an understanding of the question and connects it to plausible, real-world situations. However, the response ends abruptly, the student leaves it up to the reader to supply the resolution, and there are errors in spelling and grammar. These facts prevent it from being an exemplary response.

**SAMPLE**

*Personal Response   Write about a mystery you solved. How did you solve it?*

*There was some mud on a piece of wood in our garage. I didn't know how it got there. Nobody else knew then I saw like a hole in the mud. I remembered in science we learned about waspses, like bees. They make nests for their babies out of mud.*

## Grammar, Usage, and Mechanics

Each grammar, usage, and mechanics assessment is comprised of five multiple-choice questions worth two points each. Each question specifically relates to the lesson material for that week. Students sometimes will be asked to identify errors or incorrect constructions, so remind students to read each question carefully.

## Comprehension: Analyzing the Selection

This section of the assessment allows students to craft a longer, more detailed response to show their comprehension of what they have read. It also provides additional data on the writing skills of students as they progress through the program.

Students will sometimes be asked to respond by connecting the selection they have just read to previous selections in the unit.

These questions and prompts are worth eight points each. Use the following criteria to judge student responses. To fully answer the question or prompt, student answers should be approximately one hundred to one hundred and fifty words.

**Note:** You will notice that the rubrics below each have a two-point range. Use your professional judgment in awarding the higher point total in the scale to students' work.

### Score: 8 or 7

The student understands the question and responds suitably using the appropriate source of information. These sources include the selection itself, other selections, personal experience, opinion, prior knowledge, or plausible conjecture. The response reflects a thorough comprehension of the selection and is an acceptably complete answer to the question. The organization of the response is meaningful, it is written smoothly, and both sentences and paragraphs flow together. Paragraphs focus on related topics and are linked to one another with effective transitions. The response reads easily and demonstrates a sense of audience. It has correct spelling, grammar, usage, and mechanics, and it is written neatly and legibly.

### Score: 6 or 5

The student understands the question and responds suitably using the appropriate source of information. These sources include the selection itself, other selections, personal experience, opinion, prior knowledge, or plausible conjecture. The response may reflect comprehension of the selection or other sources and is a somewhat complete answer to the question. The organization of the response is somewhat meaningful, and both sentences and paragraphs flow together relatively smoothly. Paragraphs focus on related topics and are linked to one another with effective transitions. The response reads easily and demonstrates a sense of audience. It has occasional errors in spelling, grammar, usage, and mechanics, and it is written somewhat neatly and legibly.

### Score: 4 or 3

The student has partial understanding of the question. The response may reflect limited comprehension of the selection and is an incomplete answer to the question or includes irrelevant information. The organization of the response is weak, it is written carelessly, and both sentences and paragraphs are somewhat disorganized. Paragraphs include some extraneous information and are linked to one another ineffectively. The response requires some effort to read easily and demonstrates a poor sense of audience. It has occasional errors in spelling, grammar, usage, and mechanics, and it is written somewhat neatly and legibly.

### Score: 2 or 1

The student has minimal understanding of the question. The response may reflect poor comprehension of the selection and is a barely acceptable answer to the question or includes irrelevant information. The organization of the response is imprecise, it is written erratically, and sentences or paragraphs may be disjointed. Paragraphs may be poorly focused or are linked to one another inconsistently. The response is difficult to follow and may cause the reader to struggle. It has frequent errors in spelling, grammar, usage, and mechanics, and it is written with borderline neatness and legibility.

### Score: 0

The student fails to compose a response. If a response is attempted, it is inaccurate, meaningless, or irrelevant. The response may be written so poorly that it is neither legible nor understandable.

The following is an example of a response that would receive a score of "5" if written somewhat neatly and legibly. The student shows an understanding of the question in the opening paragraphs. The student makes few errors in spelling and grammar. However, after the opening paragraphs the focus drifts, and no mention of bridge technology is made. These facts prevent it from being an exemplary response.

### SAMPLE

*Analyzing the Selection* *How are the Golden Gate Bridge and the completion of the transcontinental railroad alike? Write about the people involved, the technology they used, and what was accomplished.*

    *The Golden Gate Bridge and the transcontinental railroad are alike because they joined things. The bridge joined land on both sides of San Francisco bay. It made it easier to cross the bay. The railroad joined the United States east to west.*

    *A lot of people worked on both things. They must have worked hard and they took a long time. I think the bridge must have been more dangerous. People could fall off the bridge.*

    *One way they were different is how they was built. The railroad had been around for a while. They put down the rails in the same way they always had with wood under the metal rails and spikes holding the rails down. It was probably hard coming over mountains because they had to make tunnels through mountains. The deserts were probably hard too.*

    *The bridge must have been really hard to make because of the deep water. It must have been scarey. I don't know how people thought of how to make the bridge.*

# Oral Fluency Assessments

## Administering Oral Fluency Assessments

The Oral Fluency Assessment is an efficient means for evaluating students' ability to read. It is simple to administer and score, yet it provides extraordinarily useful quantitative and qualitative data. You will find oral fluency assessments for each lesson. The words in the selections are of sufficient variety to allow for an analysis of the decoding and vocabulary abilities of a student and to draw inferences about a student's ability to derive meaning from the text.

Make a copy of the Oral Fluency Assessment for each student you will be assessing. Have students turn to the corresponding page in their workbooks. Be sure you have a pen or pencil, a stopwatch or other timer, and extra paper to record any observations. Briefly review the text before you begin. On the Oral Fluency Scores pages, you will record the student's name, the date of the assessment, and the results of the assessment.

Have the student sit comfortably at a table with you. Seat yourself and the student so that you can mark the assessment unobtrusively without distracting the student.

**Say:** *Here is a selection I would like you to read aloud for me. I am going to listen to you read and take some notes. The notes I take will help me learn how well you can read. You will not be graded for this, so you should not feel nervous. Read the selection carefully and do your best. Take a few minutes now to look over the selection, and then I will tell you when to begin.*

Allow time for the student to preview the story. Be sure you have a pen or pencil.

**Say:** *Are you ready?* (Check to be sure the student is ready.) *You may begin now.*

Start the timer or watch as the student begins to read. You may pronounce any proper nouns with which the student is unfamiliar. Do not count these words as errors.

**Note:** If the student becomes frustrated or makes several consecutive errors, stop the assessment.

At the end of one minute place a bracket ( ] ) at the end of the last word the student reads.

## Scoring Oral Fluency Assessments

The following guidelines will help you score the assessment accurately and consistently.

• Self-correcting should not be counted as an error.
• Repeating the same mistake should be counted as only one error.
• Hesitating for more than five seconds—at which point you would have provided the word—should count as an error.
• Become familiar with the evaluating codes before administering the Oral Fluency Assessment.

## Scoring Conventions

• Draw a line through any word that is misread. Count this as an error. If possible, note the type of error. (Misreading *short a* as *short e*, reading *get* as *jet*, and so on).
• Draw a bracket ( ] ) at the end of the last word the student reads in one minute.
• Words the student omits should be counted as errors, even if you prompt the student.
• Indicate with a caret extra words that have been inserted. If possible, write the inserted word. Count insertions as errors.
• Draw an arrow between words that have been reversed. Count these as one error.
• Students might repeat words on occasion. Do not count this behavior as an error.

## Finding the Student's Accuracy Rate

To find a student's accuracy rate, count the total number of words read in one minute. The numbers beside the passage on the teacher's page will make this an easier task. Subtract the number of errors from the total number of words read and use that figure to find the number of correct words read per minute. Then divide the correct words per minute by the total number of words read to find the accuracy rate. Record these numbers on the Reading Rate and Accuracy chart located on your Oral Fluency Assessment pages.

- Record the student's score on the Oral Fluency Scores pages and the Student Assessment Record.
- Complete the Reading Fluency scale at the bottom of your Oral Fluency Assessment page. These qualitative measures indicate your subjective judgment of how the student compares with other students who are reading at grade level.

**READING RATE AND ACCURACY**

| | |
|---|---|
| Total Words Read: | <u>130</u> |
| Number of Errors: | <u>19</u> |
| Number of Correct Words Read Per Minute (WPM): | <u>111</u> |
| Accuracy Rate: | <u>85%</u> |

(Number of Correct Words Read per Minute ÷ Total Words Read)

**READING FLUENCY**

| | Low | Average | High |
|---|---|---|---|
| Decoding ability | ○ | ○ | ● |
| Pace | ○ | ● | ○ |
| Syntax | ○ | ● | ○ |
| Self-correction | ○ | ● | ○ |
| Intonation | ○ | ○ | ● |

## Interpreting the Oral Fluency Assessments

First, compare the student's number of correct words per minute with the following chart. This will give you an idea of how the student compares with other students in the same grade at the same time of year. The data in this chart represents the approximate number of correct words read per minute a student should be reading in Grades 2–6. The two rows of numbers represent the 50th and 75th percentiles.

| | Units 1-2 | Units 3-4 | Units 5-6 | |
|---|---|---|---|---|
| **Grade 2** | 79 | 100 | 117 | 75th Percentile |
| | 51 | 72 | 89 | 50th Percentile |
| **Grade 3** | 99 | 120 | 137 | 75th Percentile |
| | 71 | 92 | 107 | 50th Percentile |
| **Grade 4** | 119 | 139 | 152 | 75th Percentile |
| | 94 | 112 | 123 | 50th Percentile |
| **Grade 5** | 139 | 156 | 168 | 75th Percentile |
| | 110 | 127 | 139 | 50th Percentile |
| **Grade 6** | 153 | 167 | 177 | 75th Percentile |
| | 127 | 140 | 150 | 50th Percentile |

**Source** Adapted from Hasbrouck, J., & Tindal, G. (2005). <u>Oral Reading Fluency: 90 Years of Measurement</u> (Tech. Rep. No. 33). Eugene, Oregon: University of Oregon, College of Education, Behavioral Research and Teaching.

Then examine the student's accuracy rate. Reading accuracy should remain constant or gradually increase within a grade and between grades, until it stabilizes at ninety percent or higher. You may find it helpful to compare a student's accuracy rate after each administration to ensure that it remains constant or increases.

Next, examine the types of errors the student is making and consider how they represent underlying student behaviors. Here are some examples:

- Inserting extra words suggests that the student understands what is read, is constructing meaning, but is reading somewhat impulsively.

- A student who refuses to attempt to read a word is probably uncertain of his or her abilities and is unwilling to take risks.

- Misreading regular letter sounds implies that the student has not yet mastered the conventions of the sound-symbol relationship. This is in contrast with the student who misreads complex letter sounds (alternate sounds, blends, diphthongs, digraphs, and so on) but has little difficulty with regular letter sounds.

Finally, consider the error pattern. If errors are scattered randomly throughout the passage, then the error types represent skills the student has not yet developed. If errors increase in frequency from beginning to end, then fatigue or inattention likely are involved.

## Other Considerations

Several strategies are available for promoting reading fluency and accuracy. These involve pairing an accomplished reader with a developing reader, small-group choral reading, and repeated readings of familiar text.

You may find it useful to establish targets for reading accuracy. These targets may include goals such as reading ten words in a row without error, increasing by increments the number of correct words a student reads in a minute, or decreasing a specific error type. Establishing such targets allows you to provide appropriate instructional support and gives students a reasonable goal.

## *End of Unit Writing Prompt*

The writing prompt offers the opportunity for an on-demand writing performance similar to the type students will encounter in high-stakes testing. Use the rubrics that follow the prompts to judge students' work. Student writing should be included in each student's Writing Portfolio.

# Teacher Records

This Teacher's Edition contains record keeping material that will help you keep track of student progress in lesson assessments.

## *Six Point Rubrics*

Six Point Writing Rubrics for assessing student writing are included.

These can take the place of the four point rubrics if you are in a school that uses the six point rubric system.

## *Oral Fluency Scores*

These pages allow you to note student accuracy rates throughout the year.

## Class Assessment Record

These pages offer a warehouse for class scores.

The spaces following the student's name allow for the recording of student scores in each lesson assessment (out of the 50-point scale) and each writing prompt (using the four point or six point rubrics to assess).

The format of the Class Assessment Record provides an easy way to monitor student growth across the year.

## Student Assessment Record

You can duplicate this page for each student and use it to track student progress.

## Comprehension Observation Log

Observing students as they read anthology selections is an effective way to learn their strengths and areas of need in comprehension. Use the Comprehension Observation Log to record your observations of students. Choose a small set of students to focus on for a particular lesson. You might want to observe students more than once to get a clear idea of their comprehension of texts. Copy this page for each student or group of students you observe.

Name _____ Date _____ Score _____

# Island of the Blue Dolphins

## Vocabulary

**Read each item. Fill in the bubble for the answer you think is correct.**

**1.** Which suffix means "state or quality of"?

Ⓐ -or

Ⓒ -ness

Ⓑ -less

Ⓓ -ful

**2.** Another word for **pursued** is

Ⓐ chased.

Ⓒ jumped.

Ⓑ rolled.

Ⓓ hungered.

**3.** Karana paddles her canoe through the **tides. Tides** are

Ⓐ large pieces of driftwood.

Ⓑ plants with their roots in the bottom of the sea.

Ⓒ schools of fish.

Ⓓ changes in the sea level.

**4.** The Island of the Blue Dolphins is **deserted.** This means that it

Ⓐ is a desert.

Ⓑ is surrounded by coral beds.

Ⓒ has no people on it.

Ⓓ has a large sandy beach.

**5.** Karana **dozed** while she was in the canoe. This means that she

Ⓐ paddled hard.

Ⓒ removed water.

Ⓑ steered.

Ⓓ slept lightly.

## Island of the Blue Dolphins (continued)

## Comprehension

**Read the following questions carefully. Then completely fill in the bubble of each correct answer. You may look back at the selection to find the answer to each of the questions.**

**1.** Where is Karana when the selection begins?

Ⓐ on a rock

Ⓑ in a canoe

Ⓒ in a cave

Ⓓ in a forest

**2.** What happens the first night Karana moves her bed?

Ⓐ She thinks she sees a ship.

Ⓑ The winds blow out of the west.

Ⓒ She has terrible dreams.

Ⓓ Dogs try to attack her.

## Island of the Blue Dolphins (continued)

3. The narrator of this selection is

Ⓐ an experienced sea captain.

Ⓑ someone telling about what they think a dolphin is seeing.

Ⓒ a girl who had been left behind accidentally.

Ⓓ an ancestor of the people living on the island.

4. From what point of view is this selection told?

Ⓐ second-person point of view

Ⓑ first-person point of view

Ⓒ third-person point of view

Ⓓ a dolphin's point of view

5. What makes Karana decide to turn back to the island?

Ⓐ It gets dark.

Ⓑ The canoe springs a leak.

Ⓒ The tides are too strong.

Ⓓ She gets very tired.

**Island of the Blue Dolphins** (continued)

**Read the following questions carefully. Use complete sentences to answer the questions.** Possible answers below

6. Why is summer the best time on the Island of the Blue Dolphins?

   The sun is warm and the winds blow milder out of the west.

7. Why does Karana become sad when the first storm of winter comes?

   She knows the ship would not come back for her in winter.

8. Why does Karana choose the smallest canoe?

   It is the easiest one for her to move.

9. How does Karana get the canoe into the water?

   She removes the rocks, fills in the holes, and lays down kelp.

10. What is different about the way Karana acts when she gets back to the island?

    She is happy to be back, even though earlier she had wanted to leave.

## Island of the Blue Dolphins (continued)

**Read the question below. Write complete sentences for your answer. Support your answer with information from the selection.**

**Linking to the Concepts** Why is Karana willing to risk going to sea in a canoe?

_____

_____

_____

_____

_____

**Read the prompt below. Your answer should be based on your own experience. Write complete sentences for your answer.**

**Personal Response** Write about a time when you were very lonely. How did you feel, and what made you feel better?

_____

_____

_____

_____

_____

## Island of the Blue Dolphins (continued)

## Grammar, Usage, and Mechanics

**Read each question. Fill in the bubble beside the answer in each group that is correct. If none of the answers is correct, choose the last answer, "none of the above."**

1. In which sentence is a noun underlined?

   Ⓐ The <u>sheep</u> walked.     Ⓒ The sheep <u>walked</u>.

   Ⓑ <u>The</u> sheep walked.     Ⓓ none of the above

2. In which sentence is a proper noun underlined?

   Ⓐ He <u>tried</u> to ski Asia.     Ⓒ He tried to ski <u>Asia</u>.

   Ⓑ He tried to <u>ski</u> Asia.     Ⓓ none of the above

3. Which sentence has correct capitalization?

   Ⓐ A picture of a great family room was in *good Housekeeping* magazine.

   Ⓑ A picture of a great family room was in *Good Housekeeping* Magazine.

   Ⓒ A picture of a great family room was in *Good Housekeeping* magazine.

   Ⓓ none of the above

4. Which sentence has a mistake in capitalization?

   Ⓐ Francis Scott Key wrote *The Star-Spangled Banner.*

   Ⓑ The *Better Business Bureau* helps people.

   Ⓒ The author of *Little Women* is Louisa May Alcott.

   Ⓓ none of the above

5. Which sentence has correct capitalization?

   Ⓐ The beaches in South carolina were beautiful.

   Ⓑ The beaches in South Carolina were beautiful.

   Ⓒ The beaches in south Carolina were beautiful.

   Ⓓ none of the above

**Island of the Blue Dolphins** (continued)

## Analyzing the Selection

**Read the questions below. Write complete sentences for your answer. Support your answer with information from the selection.**

What do you think drove Karana to work so hard to survive? What does her effort say about her willingness to take risks?

_____

_____

_____

_____

_____

_____

_____

_____

_____

_____

_____

_____

_____

## Island of the Blue Dolphins (continued)

# Oral Fluency Assessment

### *Writing a New Song*

| | |
|---|---|
| Watching Evan, Michelle was amazed by her brother. Even | 1–9 |
| though he was not yet five, he wanted to do everything himself! | 10–21 |
| Whether it was eating or getting dressed, Evan always said, "I | 22–32 |
| can do it!" | 33–35 |
|     What Michelle really wanted to do was play her guitar. She | 36–46 |
| had been practicing for a year. She could play without looking | 47–57 |
| at the strings. But for now, she had to be the babysitter. | 58–69 |
|     Then Michelle had an idea. | 70–74 |
|     "Hey, Evan," she said. "Do you want to help me make | 75–85 |
| something?" | 86 |
|     "I can do it!" said Evan. | 87–92 |
|     Michelle took her guitar from its case. She strummed the | 93–102 |
| strings. Then she said, "You and I are going to make a song." | 103–115 |
|     Evan said, "It will be a song about my bike." Then he began | 116–128 |
| to sing, "I wear a helmet when I ride my bike." | 129–139 |
|     Once they had the first line down, Evan added more lines | 140–150 |
| about passengers he took for rides on his bike. These included | 151–161 |
| ducks, bugs, and turtles. At some point, Michelle realized that | 162–171 |
| the two had been practicing the song for a really long time. She | 172–184 |
| hadn't noticed because they were having so much fun. | 185–193 |

---

**EVALUATING CODES FOR ORAL FLUENCY**

sky      (/) words read incorrectly

blue
^  sky    (^) inserted word
        ( ] ) after the last word

---

**READING RATE AND ACCURACY**

Total Words Read:        _____

Number of Errors:        _____

Number of Correct Words
Read Per Minute (WPM):     _____

Accuracy Rate:        _____

(Number of Correct Words Read per
Minute ÷ Total Words Read)

---

**READING FLUENCY**

| | Low | Average | High |
|---|---|---|---|
| Decoding ability | ○ | ○ | ○ |
| Pace | ○ | ○ | ○ |
| Syntax | ○ | ○ | ○ |
| Self-correction | ○ | ○ | ○ |
| Intonation | ○ | ○ | ○ |

**Record student rates on the Oral Fluency Scores pages.**

**UNIT 1** **Lesson 2**

Name _____ Date _____ Score _____

# Two Tickets to Freedom

## Vocabulary

**Read each item. Fill in the bubble for the answer you think is correct.**

1. **Hastened** means about the same as

   Ⓐ lifted.                    Ⓒ fastened.

   Ⓑ traveled.                  Ⓓ hurried.

2. Which prefix means "not"?

   Ⓐ *un-*                      Ⓒ *fore-*

   Ⓑ *re-*                      Ⓓ *en-*

3. "Mr. Johnson" **shuddered** when he heard that he would have to prove William was his slave. In this sentence, **shuddered** means

   Ⓐ laughed very hard.

   Ⓑ nodded slightly.

   Ⓒ absolutely refused.

   Ⓓ shook with horror.

4. A passenger in another car called to his **companion.** A **companion** is

   Ⓐ a person traveling with someone.

   Ⓑ someone who is serving a meal.

   Ⓒ a railway engineer.

   Ⓓ another word for a train conductor.

5. Ellen **concealed** her fears during the journey. This means her fears were

   Ⓐ difficult to deal with.     Ⓒ understood.

   Ⓑ hidden.                     Ⓓ not based in fact.

**Two Tickets to Freedom** (continued)

# Comprehension

Read the following questions carefully. Then completely fill in the bubble of each correct answer. You may look back at the selection to find the answer to each of the questions.

**1.** Why had William and Ellen been saving money?

Ⓐ to buy a horse and buggy

Ⓑ to buy their freedom from their master

Ⓒ to buy train tickets north

Ⓓ to buy disguises

**2.** What happens after the bell rings?

Ⓐ William is stopped by an officer.

Ⓑ The passengers look at William, Ellen, and the officer.

Ⓒ The train arrives in Baltimore.

Ⓓ William relays some bad news.

**Two Tickets to Freedom** (continued)

3. Why does Ellen board a ferry?

   (A) to escape Charleston

   (B) to see what a ferry ride was like

   (C) to cross a river

   (D) to get away from William

4. Which of these is an opinion from the selection?

   (A) They heard that there had been pickpockets in Philadelphia.

   (B) A free black man recommended a boardinghouse in Philadelphia.

   (C) The officer seemed agitated.

   (D) Ellen is dressed as a man.

5. Why does Ellen cry when they leave the station?

   (A) She is happy that they are safe.

   (B) She has left her bag on the train.

   (C) She has hurt her arm.

   (D) She is sad to be leaving her friends and family behind.

**Two Tickets to Freedom** (continued)

**Read the following questions carefully. Use complete sentences to answer the questions.** Possible answers below

6. Why are the other passengers so interested in what is happening to William and Ellen?

   The officer is holding up the train; they feel sorry for "Mr. Johnson."

7. What conclusions can you draw based on how the conductor treats William and "Mr. Johnson"?

   The conductor does not approve of slavery.

8. Why do the other men give William so much advice about how to escape from his master?

   They thought that any slave would want to escape his master.

9. Why does Ellen not have any money?

   She had given it to William because they had heard about pickpockets.

10. Where do William and Ellen go after they get off the train in Philadelphia?

    They go to an abolitionist's boardinghouse.

**Two Tickets to Freedom** (continued)

**Read the question below. Write complete sentences for your answer. Support your answer with information from the selection.**

**Linking to the Concepts** Why do you think William and Ellen took such a risk?

_____

_____

_____

_____

_____

**Read the question below. Your answer should be based on your own experience. Write complete sentences for your answer.**

**Personal Response** Have you ever taken a risk hoping it would make something in your life better? Write about what you did.

_____

_____

_____

_____

_____

**Two Tickets to Freedom** (continued)

## Grammar, Usage, and Mechanics

**Read each question. Fill in the bubble beside the answer in each group that is correct. If none of the answers is correct, choose the last answer, "none of the above."**

**1.** In which sentence is the verb underlined?

&#9398; The dog stretched.  &#9400; The <u>dog</u> stretched.

&#9399; The dog <u>stretched</u>.  &#9401; none of the above

**2.** In which sentence is an action verb underlined?

&#9398; Some ducks <u>had</u> landed on the pond.

&#9399; The pond <u>appeared</u> to be a little low.

&#9400; A frog <u>jumped</u> into the pond.

&#9401; none of the above

**3.** In which sentence is a helping verb underlined?

&#9398; The train <u>will</u> arrive in a few minutes.

&#9399; Some passengers <u>read</u> newspapers while they waited.

&#9400; The station <u>seemed</u> less crowded than usual.

&#9401; none of the above

**4.** In which sentence is a linking verb underlined?

&#9398; A car <u>damaged</u> a utility line.

&#9399; The room suddenly <u>became</u> dark.

&#9400; The power <u>will</u> return shortly.

&#9401; none of the above

**5.** In which sentence is the complete verb phrase underlined?

&#9398; The truck driver was driving on <u>the side of the road</u>.

&#9399; The truck <u>driver was</u> driving on the side of the road.

&#9400; <u>The truck driver</u> was driving on the side of the road.

&#9401; none of the above

**Two Tickets to Freedom** (continued)

## Analyzing the Selection

**Read the question below. Write complete sentences for your answer. Support your answer with information from the selection.**

At which point in the selection do you think William and Ellen were in the greatest danger of being discovered? Use information from the selection to support your opinion.

_____

_____

_____

_____

_____

_____

_____

_____

_____

_____

_____

_____

_____

## Two Tickets to Freedom (continued)

## Oral Fluency Assessment

### *The Alpha Dog*

| | |
|---|---|
| Andy and his cousin, Jake, walked into the living room. | 1–10 |
| "Max, get off the couch!" yelled Andy. | 11–17 |
| The big-eared dog opened his eyes for a moment. He let out a | 18–31 |
| long sigh and closed his eyes again. | 32–38 |
| "Andy, you really have a problem with your dog," said Jake. | 39–49 |
| "He hasn't learned who the alpha dog in this house is." | 50–60 |
| "What's an alpha dog, Jake? Is that anything like an alpha | 61–71 |
| bet?" Andy asked with a grin. | 72–77 |
| "You really have to know how dogs think in order to get | 78–89 |
| them to do what you want. Dogs are in the same animal family | 90–102 |
| as wolves. Wolves hunt and travel in packs, following a lead | 103–113 |
| wolf that is the strongest male in the pack. When two wolves or | 114–126 |
| dogs meet, the weaker one may lie down and show his throat. | 127–138 |
| This tells the stronger animal the other one doesn't want to | 139–149 |
| fight. The strongest animal in the pack is known as the alpha, | 150–161 |
| like the letter *A*. If you want Max to listen to you, he has to | 162–176 |
| know that you are the alpha dog," said Jake. | 177–185 |

**EVALUATING CODES FOR ORAL FLUENCY**

sky    (/) words read incorrectly

blue
^  sky    (^) inserted word
           ( ] ) after the last word

**READING RATE AND ACCURACY**

Total Words Read: _____

Number of Errors: _____

Number of Correct Words
Read Per Minute (WPM): _____

Accuracy Rate: _____

(Number of Correct Words Read per
Minute ÷ Total Words Read)

**READING FLUENCY**

| | Low | Average | High |
|---|---|---|---|
| Decoding ability | ○ | ○ | ○ |
| Pace | ○ | ○ | ○ |
| Syntax | ○ | ○ | ○ |
| Self-correction | ○ | ○ | ○ |
| Intonation | ○ | ○ | ○ |

**Record student rates on the Oral Fluency Scores pages.**

Name _____ Date _____ Score _____

# Mrs. Frisby and the Crow

## Vocabulary

**Read each item. Fill in the bubble for the answer you think is correct.**

**1.** What does the suffix **-ful** mean?

   Ⓐ made of        Ⓒ full of

   Ⓑ state of        Ⓓ without

**2.** Another word for **merriment** is

   Ⓐ sleep.        Ⓒ sadness.

   **Ⓑ** fun.        Ⓓ work.

**3.** Mrs. Frisby **recalled** something her husband told her. In this sentence, **recalled** means

   Ⓐ heard.

   **Ⓑ** remembered.

   Ⓒ forgot.

   Ⓓ disregarded.

**4.** Mrs. Frisby began **gnawing** the string. **Gnawing** means

   Ⓐ pulling.

   Ⓑ twisting.

   Ⓒ untangling.

   **Ⓓ** chewing.

**5.** There was not any **cover** nearby. **Cover** is

   **Ⓐ** somewhere to hide.

   Ⓑ something to eat.

   Ⓒ somewhere to visit.

   Ⓓ something to use as medicine.

**Mrs. Frisby and the Crow** (continued)

## Comprehension

**Read the following questions carefully. Then completely fill in the bubble of each correct answer. You may look back at the selection to find the answer to each of the questions.**

**1.** Who is Mrs. Frisby?

Ⓐ a farmer's wife

Ⓑ a movie actress

Ⓒ a mouse

Ⓓ a cat

**2.** Mrs. Frisby stops because

Ⓐ she sees the cat.

Ⓑ she sees a crow.

Ⓒ she drops her package.

Ⓓ she has to go around a large rock.

**Mrs. Frisby and the Crow** (continued)

**3.** Mrs. Frisby takes the straighter route home because

(A) it is less dangerous.

(B) she wants to visit with friends.

(C) she wants to be home by dark.

(D) it is prettier than the other route.

**4.** How are Mrs. Frisby and the crow alike?

(A) Both are caught on the fence.

(B) Both are very young.

(C) Both are not afraid of the dark.

(D) Both are afraid of the cat.

**5.** The author wrote this selection in order to

(A) show that if we help somebody, they might help us.

(B) tell readers how crows are attracted to shiny things.

(C) inform us how to take care of pets.

(D) prove that cats are dangerous animals.

**Mrs. Frisby and the Crow** (continued)

**Read the following questions carefully. Use complete sentences to answer the questions.** Possible answers below

**6.** What is the difference between the two routes Mrs. Frisby has to choose between?

One route was longer and would get her home after dark. One route was shorter, but was dangerous.

**7.** How does the crow get caught?

The string gets tangled on his leg, and he gets tangled in the fence.

**8.** Why does Mrs. Frisby tell the crow to stay still?

She does not want him to attract the cat's attention.

**9.** What does Mrs. Frisby think of the crow?

She thinks that he is very young and that he is foolish.

**10.** How does the crow help Mrs. Frisby?

He has her climb on his back so they can both fly away from the cat.

## Mrs. Frisby and the Crow (continued)

**Read the question below. Write complete sentences for your answer. Support your answer with information from the selection.**

**Linking to the Concepts** Why does the crow feel that he is in debt to Mrs. Frisby?

_____

_____

_____

_____

_____

_____

**Read the prompt below. Your answer should be based on your own experience. Write complete sentences for your answer.**

**Personal Response** Write about a risk you took to help someone else. Why do you think you did it?

_____

_____

_____

_____

_____

_____

**Mrs. Frisby and the Crow** (continued)

## Grammar, Usage, and Mechanics

**Read each question. Fill in the bubble beside the answer in each group that is correct. If none of the answers is correct, choose the last answer, "none of the above."**

1. Which sentence has a correct plural form?
   - Ⓐ Some girles were playing soccer in the park.
   - Ⓑ Patchs of sunlight shone on the ground.
   - Ⓒ A team of horses pulled a wagon along the trail.
   - Ⓓ none of the above

2. Which sentence has a correct plural form?
   - Ⓐ Childs were playing.
   - Ⓒ Her tooths hurt.
   - Ⓑ We shared the cookies.
   - Ⓓ none of the above

3. Which sentence has an action verb?
   - Ⓐ The spies wrote in secret code.
   - Ⓑ People have radios for the news.
   - Ⓒ The new park had six benches.
   - Ⓓ none of the above

4. Which sentence has a linking verb?
   - Ⓐ Tomatoes make pizza sauce.
   - Ⓑ In the country, drivers watch for deer after dusk.
   - Ⓒ Some Chinese emperors are famous.
   - Ⓓ none of the above

5. Which sentence has a correct plural form?
   - Ⓐ It is difficult to paint around the doores.
   - Ⓑ The baker made extra loaves during the holidays.
   - Ⓒ The family had mouses in the garage.
   - Ⓓ none of the above

**Mrs. Frisby and the Crow** (continued)

## Analyzing the Selection

**Read the question below. Write complete sentences for your answer. Support your answer with information from the selections.**

Think about the selections "Island of the Blue Dolphin," "Two Tickets to Freedom," and "Mrs. Frisby and the Crow." How are the risks in the selections similar, and how are they different?

_____

_____

_____

_____

_____

_____

_____

_____

_____

_____

_____

_____

## Mrs. Frisby and the Crow (continued)

## Oral Fluency Assessment

### *Bats*

| | |
|---|---|
| There are many different types of bats. They are found | 1–10 |
| in almost every part of the world. Bats usually live in caves | 11–22 |
| and other dark places. Some live in trees and look like leaves | 23–34 |
| hanging from the limbs. Bats might live in barns, under bridges | 35–45 |
| or even in houses. Because they are small and they can bend | 46–57 |
| easily, bats can get into a house through a small opening. | 58–68 |
| Bats sleep during the day. They fly at night to hunt for food. | 69–81 |
| Their main food is flying insects. Some bats eat fruit, and some | 82–93 |
| eat both fruit and insects. In the United States, bats are helpful | 94–105 |
| because they eat so many insects. Some people build houses for | 106–116 |
| the bats. They want the bats nearby so they will eat insects that | 117–129 |
| bother people, their crops, and their pets. | 130–136 |
| When it is dark, bats have no trouble finding their way | 137–147 |
| around. They fly when there is no light, yet they do not bump | 148–160 |
| into things or crash. Bats do this by sending out sounds. The | 161–172 |
| sounds echo, or bounce back, off walls or objects and let the | 173–184 |
| bats fly past without being hurt. | 185–190 |

---

**EVALUATING CODES
FOR ORAL FLUENCY**

sky        (/) words read incorrectly

blue

^   sky    (^) inserted word

         ( ] ) after the last word

---

**READING RATE AND ACCURACY**

Total Words Read:      _____

Number of Errors:      _____

Number of Correct Words
Read Per Minute (WPM):    _____

Accuracy Rate:      _____

(Number of Correct Words Read per
Minute ÷ Total Words Read)

---

**READING FLUENCY**

| | Low | Average | High |
|---|---|---|---|
| Decoding ability | ○ | ○ | ○ |
| Pace | ○ | ○ | ○ |
| Syntax | ○ | ○ | ○ |
| Self-correction | ○ | ○ | ○ |
| Intonation | ○ | ○ | ○ |

**Record student rates on the Oral Fluency Scores pages.**

Name _____ Date _____ Score _____

# Langston Hughes: Poet of the People

## Vocabulary

**Read each item. Fill in the bubble for the answer you think is correct.**

1. The inflectional ending **-ed** in *arrived* tells you that the action

   Ⓐ is happening now.          Ⓒ happened in the past.

   Ⓑ cannot happen.            Ⓓ will happen in the future.

2. Another word for **pleading** is

   Ⓐ smiling.                  Ⓒ questioning.

   Ⓑ begging.                  Ⓓ running.

3. Langston went to Mexico so that he could have more **opportunities**. What are **opportunities**?

   Ⓐ invitations to parties    Ⓒ chances to succeed

   Ⓑ types of food             Ⓓ types of clothing

4. Thad is earning a medical degree so that he can make a **decent** living someday. A **decent** living is one that is

   Ⓐ fairly comfortable.

   Ⓑ requires travel.

   Ⓒ easy to accomplish.

   Ⓓ related to medicine.

5. Langston **paces** as his father looks through the ledger. He is

   Ⓐ staring off into space.   Ⓒ thinking of a good excuse.

   Ⓑ eating a snack.           Ⓓ walking back and forth.

**Langston Hughes: Poet of the People** (continued)

## Comprehension

**Read the following questions carefully. Then completely fill in the bubble of each correct answer. You may look back at the selection to find the answer to each of the questions.**

**1.** Where does Langston's father want to send him?

Ⓐ Mexico

Ⓑ Cleveland

Ⓒ Harlem

Ⓓ Switzerland

**2.** What happens right after Mr. Hughes sees one of Langston's poems on the floor?

Ⓐ He crumples the paper.

Ⓑ He reads the poem.

Ⓒ He puts the paper in a drawer.

Ⓓ He decides that Langston will go to school to be an engineer.

## Langston Hughes: Poet of the People (continued)

**3.** Which of these is fact and not an opinion about Columbia University?

   Ⓐ It has good writing teachers.

   **Ⓑ** It is in New York City.

   Ⓒ It is one of the best schools in the nation.

   Ⓓ It has a beautiful campus.

**4.** Thad is studying to become a doctor because

   **Ⓐ** he wants a comfortable life.

   Ⓑ he wants to help people.

   Ⓒ his best subject was biology.

   Ⓓ his father wants him to become a doctor.

**5.** What is Langston going to do at the end of the selection?

   Ⓐ He is going back to Mexico with his father.

   Ⓑ He is going to finish his engineering degree.

   **Ⓒ** He is going to move to Harlem to write.

   Ⓓ He is going to study medicine instead of engineering.

**UNIT 1 Lesson 4**

**Langston Hughes: Poet of the People** (continued)

**Read the following questions carefully. Use complete sentences to answer the questions.** Possible answers below

6. How are Langston and his father different from one another?

   Langston is a writer and a dreamer. His practical father runs a ranch.

7. Why did the author write this play?

   The author wrote it to show that people sometimes need to take risks.

8. What will Langston's father do if his son leaves school?

   If Langston leaves school, his father will not give him any more money.

9. How are Langston and Thad different?

   Langston wants to be a writer; Thad wants to be a doctor and earn a good living.

10. Why is this selection called "Langston Hughes: Poet of the People"?

    It tells about how Hughes wanted to write about African American life.

## Langston Hughes: Poet of the People (continued)

**Read the question below. Write complete sentences for your answer. Support your answer with information from the selection.**

**Linking to the Concepts** Why does Hughes's father doubt that his son will be successful as a writer?

_____

_____

_____

_____

_____

**Read the questions below. Your answer should be based on your own experience. Write complete sentences for your answer.**

**Personal Response** What is you idea of success? How is it different from what your friends and family think of as success?

_____

_____

_____

_____

_____

**Langston Hughes: Poet of the People** (continued)

## Grammar, Usage, and Mechanics

**Read each question. Fill in the bubble beside the answer in each group that is correct. If none of the answers is correct, choose the last answer, "none of the above."**

**1.** In which sentence is the object of the verb underlined?

Ⓐ <u>Workers</u> built the house. Ⓒ Workers built the <u>house</u>.

Ⓑ Workers <u>built</u> the house. Ⓓ none of the above

**2.** In which sentence is the object of the verb underlined?

Ⓐ The <u>mill</u> ground the grain into flour.

Ⓑ The mill <u>ground</u> the grain into flour.

Ⓒ The mill ground the grain into <u>flour</u>.

Ⓓ none of the above

**3.** In which sentence is the object of the verb a pronoun?

Ⓐ A friend of my family is looking for a new job.

Ⓑ A company called him two times last week.

Ⓒ It is a good job that will involve lots of travel.

Ⓓ none of the above

**4.** Which sentence is correct?

Ⓐ Laura and Eve gave her birthday presents.

Ⓑ I read about sheeps in <u>time</u>.

Ⓒ We bought shelfs in Miami, Florida.

Ⓓ none of the above

**5.** In which sentence is the object of the verb underlined?

Ⓐ Some <u>people</u> borrow money from their friends.

Ⓑ Some people borrow money from their <u>friends</u>.

Ⓒ Some people borrow <u>money</u> from their friends.

Ⓓ none of the above

**Langston Hughes: Poet of the People** (continued)

## Analyzing the Selection

**Read the questions below. Write complete sentences for your answer. Support your answer with information from the selection.**

What do you think caused Hughes to choose the life path that he did? Did he really take risks, or was he sure of his success?

_____

_____

_____

_____

_____

_____

_____

_____

_____

_____

_____

_____

_____

## Langston Hughes: Poet of the People (continued)

## Oral Fluency Assessment

### *The Jade Plant*

| | |
|---|---|
| Some plants are very easy to grow. The jade plant is one of | 1–13 |
| them. These green plants originally came from South Africa, | 14–22 |
| but they grow well indoors in other places. | 23–30 |
| Since they come from a dry area, they need less water | 31–41 |
| than most plants. Their thick, fleshy leaves can be oval or | 42–52 |
| round. Their color ranges from coppery green to dark green to | 53–63 |
| blue-gray. | 64–65 |
| Jade plants bloom during winter when the days are shorter. | 66–75 |
| The lack of light causes them to flower. The plants often do not | 76–88 |
| bloom in rooms where lights are turned on at night. If the room | 89–101 |
| is dark at night, clusters of pink and white star-shaped flowers | 102–113 |
| appear on the smooth, trunk-like, brown branches. | 114–121 |
| Jade plants do need some sunlight. They should have four | 122–131 |
| or more hours of sunshine during the day. Plants that have | 132–142 |
| not always been kept in direct sun need to adjust slowly. | 143–153 |
| Otherwise, they will get sunburned. | 154–158 |
| Most jade plants live a long time. They are nice small plants, | 159–170 |
| but they can also grow quite large. Some of them become | 171–181 |
| bushes or trees that may grow as high as five feet tall. | 182–193 |

**EVALUATING CODES
FOR ORAL FLUENCY**

sky          (/) words read incorrectly

blue
  ^  sky    (^) inserted word
               ( ] ) after the last word

---

**READING RATE AND ACCURACY**

Total Words Read:          _____

Number of Errors:          _____

Number of Correct Words
Read Per Minute (WPM):   _____

Accuracy Rate:              _____

(Number of Correct Words Read per
Minute ÷ Total Words Read)

---

**READING FLUENCY**

| | Low | Average | High |
|---|---|---|---|
| Decoding ability | ○ | ○ | ○ |
| Pace | ○ | ○ | ○ |
| Syntax | ○ | ○ | ○ |
| Self-correction | ○ | ○ | ○ |
| Intonation | ○ | ○ | ○ |

**Record student rates on the Oral Fluency Scores pages.**

Name _____ Date _____ Score _____

# Daedalus and Icarus

## Vocabulary

**Read each item. Fill in the bubble for the answer you think is correct.**

**1.** Something that is **brilliant** is

Ⓐ bright.　　　　　Ⓒ heavy.

Ⓑ unhealthy.　　　Ⓓ tall.

**2.** All of these are examples of compound words EXCEPT

Ⓐ icehouse.　　　　Ⓒ icing.

Ⓑ ice cream.　　　　Ⓓ ice-cold.

**3.** Birds had only to **spread** their wings to leave Crete. In this sentence, **spread** means

Ⓐ open outward.

Ⓑ flap.

Ⓒ flatten.

Ⓓ remove feathers from.

**4.** Daedalus **nudged** Icarus from the windowsill. **Nudged** means about the same as

Ⓐ lifted suddenly.

Ⓑ dangled on a rope.

Ⓒ forced to climb.

Ⓓ pushed slightly.

**5.** The palace is **luxurious.** This means the palace is

Ⓐ behind a high wall.

Ⓑ rich and comfortable.

Ⓒ visible from far away.

Ⓓ dingy and dirty.

**UNIT 1**  **Lesson 5**

## Daedalus and Icarus (continued)

## Comprehension

**Read the following questions carefully. Then completely fill in the bubble of each correct answer. You may look back at the selection to find the answer to each of the questions.**

**1.** Who are Daedalus and Icarus?

   Ⓐ a king and prince

   Ⓑ two wandering hunters

   Ⓒ prisoners

   Ⓓ palace guards

**2.** Why is Daedalus unhappy when the selection begins?

   Ⓐ He and Icarus are not free.

   Ⓑ He is not given enough food.

   Ⓒ He cannot fly.

   Ⓓ He is given hard work to do.

**Daedalus and Icarus** (continued)

3. How is the palace like a bird cage?

Ⓐ Birds live in both places.

Ⓑ There are bars on both things.

Ⓒ Both are built out of metal.

Ⓓ Things are shut inside both.

4. Daedalus warns Icarus about

Ⓐ flying too close to the sun.

Ⓑ eating the food from inside the palace.

Ⓒ flying too low so that they will be seen.

Ⓓ talking to gulls.

5. Why does Icarus fall into the sea?

Ⓐ He jumped out of the tower.

Ⓑ The wax in the wings melted.

Ⓒ The gulls could not catch him.

Ⓓ He was hunting for fish the way a gull does.

## Daedalus and Icarus (continued)

**Read the following questions carefully. Use complete sentences to answer the questions.** Possible answers below

**6.** How are Daedalus and Icarus different?

Icarus does not mind living in the palace, but Daedalus does.

**7.** Why does Icarus laugh at his father?

He knows the only way to get off an island is to fly, and they cannot fly.

**8.** Why does it take Daedalus so long to make the wings?

He must get the feathers from birds one at a time.

**9.** What happens after the seagulls peck at Icarus?

He flies higher so that they cannot reach him.

**10.** Why is Daedalus unhappy at the end of the selection?

He is free, but he is now alone.

**Daedalus and Icarus** (continued)

**Read the question below. Write complete sentences for your answer. Support your answer with information from the selection.**

**Linking to the Concepts** Why was the risk Icarus took a bad choice?

_____

_____

_____

_____

_____

**Read the prompt below. Your response should be based on your own experience. Write complete sentences for your response.**

**Personal Response** Write about a risk you took that seemed like a good choice at first but turned out to be a bad one. Explain how you discovered it was a bad choice.

_____

_____

_____

_____

_____

**Daedalus and Icarus** (continued)

## Grammar, Usage, and Mechanics

**Read each question. Fill in the bubble beside the answer in each group that is correct. If none of the answers is correct, choose the last answer, "none of the above."**

**1.** In which sentence is the subject of the verb underlined?

Ⓐ The <u>officer</u> told the drivers to turn left.

Ⓑ The officer told the <u>drivers</u> to turn left.

Ⓒ The officer told the drivers to turn <u>left</u>.

Ⓓ none of the above

**2.** In which sentence is the verb underlined?

Ⓐ <u>Jim</u> blocked a shot.    Ⓒ Jim <u>blocked</u> a shot.

Ⓑ Jim blocked a <u>shot</u>.    Ⓓ none of the above

**3.** In which sentence is the use of underlining correct?

Ⓐ Jean read the book, The <u>Monsters and Me</u>.

Ⓑ Jean read <u>the book, The Monsters and Me</u>.

Ⓒ Jean read the book, <u>The Monsters</u> and Me.

Ⓓ none of the above

**4.** In which sentence is underlining used correctly?

Ⓐ Judy Wolfman wrote <u>Life on a Pig Farm</u>.

Ⓑ <u>Judy Wolfman</u> has written many books.

Ⓒ The <u>Lancaster Public Library</u> has many of her books.

Ⓓ none of the above

**5.** In which sentence is the use of italics correct?

Ⓐ Most people liked the movie *Run Like the Wind*.

Ⓑ *Emerson van Lep* was the director of this movie.

Ⓒ The movie was shown at *Northside Cineplex*.

Ⓓ none of the above

**Daedalus and Icarus** (continued)

## Analyzing the Selection

**Read the question below. Write complete sentences for your answer. Support your answer with information from the selections.**

How was the risk that Icarus took different from the risks taken by the characters in the other unit selections?

_____

_____

_____

_____

_____

_____

_____

_____

_____

_____

_____

_____

_____

_____

_____

## Daedalus and Icarus (continued)

# Oral Fluency Assessment

### *Wheelchair Basketball*

| | |
|---|---|
| The Dallas Hotshots is a basketball team for children in | 1–10 |
| wheelchairs. The children use wheelchairs specially designed | 11–17 |
| for playing sports. The chairs are not very heavy and have | 18–28 |
| angled wheels and wheel guards so fingers won't get caught | 29–38 |
| in spokes. | 39–40 |
| Players come from all over the city of Dallas. "When I first | 41–52 |
| started, I felt bad," said Kate Miller. "I couldn't pick up the ball | 53–65 |
| or shoot the ball. Then I made my first basket, and I didn't ever | 66–79 |
| want to stop." John Cole agreed with her and said, "That's the | 80–91 |
| way I was. I thought the other kids would pick on me. But they | 92–105 |
| aren't that way." | 106–108 |
| Ford Jones, the team's coach, is also in a wheelchair. "You | 109–119 |
| have to be able to wheel the chair and dribble at the same time. | 120–133 |
| Then you have to bend over quickly to scoop up the ball while | 134–146 |
| still moving," he explained. "The wheelchair is like part of your | 147–157 |
| body, so when you guard and block a player you have to be | 158–170 |
| careful about where you place your chair. That's probably the | 171–180 |
| hardest thing to do. You must work hard to get it right," he said. | 181–194 |

**EVALUATING CODES FOR ORAL FLUENCY**

sky      (/) words read incorrectly

blue

^   sky    (^) inserted word

         ( ] ) after the last word

**READING RATE AND ACCURACY**

Total Words Read: _____

Number of Errors: _____

Number of Correct Words
Read Per Minute (WPM): _____

Accuracy Rate: _____

(Number of Correct Words Read per
Minute ÷ Total Words Read)

**READING FLUENCY**

| | Low | Average | High |
|---|---|---|---|
| Decoding ability | O | O | O |
| Pace | O | O | O |
| Syntax | O | O | O |
| Self-correction | O | O | O |
| Intonation | O | O | O |

**Record student rates on the Oral Fluency Scores pages.**

Name _____  Date _____  Score _____

# Narrative Writing

## Writing Situation
A story about how you or someone you know took a risk

## Audience
Your classmates

## Directions for Writing
All of us have done something risky. It might be something such as being in a spelling bee or going someplace that seemed scary. Write about a time you or someone you know took a risk and what happened as a result.

## Checklist
You will earn the best score if you
- think about your ideas and plan your writing before you begin.
- write in a way that is interesting to your readers.
- use sensory words so the reader can experience what happened.
- write paragraphs that have a topic sentence and focus on related ideas.
- vary your sentences and the words you use.
- tell about the characters in your story.
- tell about the place where the story happens.
- tell events in the order they happen.
- use subjects, verbs, and modifiers correctly.
- write complete sentences and avoid fragments or run-ons.

# Four Point Rubrics for Narrative Writing

| Genre | 1 Point | 2 Points | 3 Points | 4 Points |
|---|---|---|---|---|
| Narrative | Narrative has missing details or elements. Logical order and narrative structure is unclear. Plot does not include a viable problem. Character development is not apparent. Setting does not include descriptions of where and when the narrative is set. | Narrative includes plot outline and some descriptive details and elements that add excitement or color, but narrative structure is not entirely clear. Character development is minimal. Setting includes minimal descriptions of where and when the narrative is set. | Narrative includes fairly well developed plot with descriptive details and other elements such as subplots that are integrated into the resolution. Narrative structure is clear. Characters are developed, though some characters may seem superficial. Setting includes descriptions of where and when the narrative is set. | Narrative includes more complicated plot lines with varied timelines, flashbacks, or dual story lines. Narrative structure is well defined. Characters well defined throughout, with unique qualities integral to the plot. Setting includes detailed descriptions of where and when the narrative is set. |
| Narrative: Theme | No theme is apparent. | Superficial theme is included but not integrated. | A theme is expressed but not well developed. | The narrative fully develops a theme that expresses an underlying message beyond the narrative plot. |
| **Writing Traits** | | | | |
| Audience | Displays little or no sense of audience. Does not engage audience. | Displays some sense of audience. | Writes with audience in mind throughout. | Displays a strong sense of audience. Engages audience. |
| Voice | The writing provides little sense of involvement or commitment. There is no evidence that the writer has chosen a suitable voice. | The writer's commitment to the topic seems inconsistent. A sense of the writer may emerge at times; however, the voice is either inappropriately personal or inappropriately impersonal. | A voice is present. The writer demonstrates commitment to the topic. In places, the writing is expressive, engaging, or sincere. Words and expressions are clear and precise. | The writer has chosen a voice appropriate for the topic, purpose, and audience. Unique style comes through. The writing is expressive, engaging, or sincere. Strong commitment to the topic. |
| **Writing Conventions** | | | | |
| Conventions Overall | Numerous errors in usage, grammar, spelling, capitalization, and punctuation repeatedly distract the reader and make the text difficult to read. The reader finds it difficult to focus on the message. | The writing demonstrates limited control of standard writing conventions (punctuation, spelling, capitalization, grammar, and usage). Errors sometimes impede readability. | The writing demonstrates control of standard writing conventions (punctuation, spelling, capitalization, grammar, and usage). Minor errors, while perhaps noticeable, do not impede readability. | The writing demonstrates exceptionally strong control of standard writing conventions (punctuation, spelling, capitalization, grammar, and usage) and uses them effectively to enhance communication. Errors are so few and so minor that the reader can easily skim over them. |

Name _____ Date _____ Score _____

# The Snowflake: A Water Cycle Story

## Vocabulary

**Read each item. Fill in the bubble for the answer you think is correct.**

1. If something is **raging,** it is

   Ⓐ quiet.

   Ⓑ peaceful.

   Ⓒ wild.

   Ⓓ colorful.

2. What does the Greek root **bio** mean?

   Ⓐ life

   Ⓑ heat

   Ⓒ light

   Ⓓ water

3. The snowflake falls onto the **jagged** peak of a mountain. In this sentence, **jagged** means

   Ⓐ highest.

   Ⓑ sharp and pointed.

   Ⓒ smooth and rounded.

   Ⓓ tree-lined.

4. The water droplet gets into the **irrigation** system of a farm. An **irrigation** system

   Ⓐ feeds the animals on a farm.

   Ⓑ supplies water to a farm.

   Ⓒ fuels the farm machinery.

   Ⓓ harvests the crops on a farm.

5. The water droplet may have been in a **glacier** for many years. A **glacier** is

   Ⓐ a series of pipes.

   Ⓑ a storage tank.

   Ⓒ a small underground stream.

   Ⓓ a huge mass of ice.

**The Snowflake: A Water Cycle Story** (continued)

## Comprehension

**Read the following questions carefully. Then completely fill in the bubble of each correct answer. You may look back at the selection to find the answer to each of the questions.**

**1.** What happens right after the ice in the pond melts?

Ⓐ The snowflake becomes a water droplet.

Ⓑ A water droplet goes through a series of smaller and smaller pipes.

Ⓒ A water droplet spills over a waterfall.

Ⓓ There is fog in the morning.

**2.** Why does the droplet stop and start again when it is in the small pipe?

Ⓐ The water level in the reservoir is rising and falling.

Ⓑ Waves are making the motion of the water.

Ⓒ The water faucet is being turned off and on.

Ⓓ It is normal for water to stop flowing and then start again.

### The Snowflake: A Water Cycle Story (continued)

3. Which of these is NOT a form that the water droplet took on its journey?

   Ⓐ part of a frozen pond

   Ⓑ a cloud

   Ⓒ a puddle

   Ⓓ part of a stream

4. Why is the droplet going through filters after it gets to the reservoir?

   Ⓐ to add chemicals

   Ⓑ to remove dirt particles

   Ⓒ to keep the droplet from evaporating

   Ⓓ to lower the water level in the reservoir

5. The main character in this selection is

   Ⓐ a farmer.

   Ⓑ a young girl.

   Ⓒ a fish.

   Ⓓ a snowflake.

**The Snowflake: A Water Cycle Story** (continued)

**Read the following questions carefully. Use complete sentences to answer the questions.** Possible answers below

**6.** Why did the author write this selection?

The author wrote the selection to show the different forms that water takes and how it gets from place to place.

**7.** What is the difference between a water droplet and a snowflake?

A snowflake is the form a water droplet takes when it freezes.

**8.** How did the water droplet get to the farm?

It was pumped through a pipe from the river.

**9.** What happens to the water droplet after it gets into the mouth of a fish?

It goes through the fish's body and back to the sea.

**10.** How are pipes used in the selection?

Pipes take water to places where people can use it.

**The Snowflake: A Water Cycle Story** (continued)

**Read the question below. Write complete sentences for your answer. Support your answer with information from the selection.**

**Linking to the Concepts** What do you think might happen to the snowflake next?

_____

_____

_____

_____

_____

**Read the question below. Your answer should be based on your own experience. Write complete sentences for your answer.**

**Personal Response** What are the ways you use water in your daily life?

_____

_____

_____

_____

_____

_____

**The Snowflake: A Water Cycle Story** (continued)

## Grammar, Usage, and Mechanics

**Read each question. Fill in the bubble beside the answer in each group that is correct. If none of the answers is correct, choose the last answer, "none of the above."**

**1.** Which sentence has correct capitalization?

Ⓐ Manx cats do not have tails.

Ⓑ kittens can be very playful.

Ⓒ some people prefer dogs.

Ⓓ none of the above

**2.** Which sentence has correct punctuation?

Ⓐ Yesterday Leda gave out party invitations?

Ⓑ The party will be held at the skating rink.

Ⓒ I have a soccer game on Saturday, so I will not go

Ⓓ none of the above

**3.** Which sentence has an object pronoun?

Ⓐ I love basketball.

Ⓑ Dave is our point guard.

Ⓒ He passes it quickly.

Ⓓ none of the above

**4.** Which sentence has the subject underlined?

Ⓐ That was an amazing <u>goal</u>!

Ⓑ Do you <u>think</u> we will win this game?

Ⓒ The score was <u>even</u> at with a minute to go.

Ⓓ none of the above

**5.** What must you do at the start of a paragraph?

Ⓐ use italics          Ⓒ indent

Ⓑ underline          Ⓓ none of the above

**The Snowflake: A Water Cycle Story** (continued)

## Analyzing the Selection

**Read the question below. Write complete sentences for your answer. Support your answer with information from the selection.**

A drop of water in a pond near your house ends up in a glass of water in a house in China. How might this happen? Use information from the selection and your imagination to write your answer.

_____

_____

_____

_____

_____

_____

_____

_____

_____

_____

_____

## The Snowflake: A Water Cycle Story (continued)

## Oral Fluency Assessment

### *An Adobe Wall*

| | |
|---|---|
| Mr. Jones wants to build a wall in front of his family's house. | 1–13 |
| He wants to make it with adobe bricks. This is an inexpensive | 14–25 |
| and attractive building material. Adobe bricks have been used | 26–34 |
| for thousands of years. Many houses in the Southwest are made | 35–45 |
| with adobe bricks. | 46–48 |
| To make the bricks, Mr. Jones mixes dirt with water. This | 49–59 |
| makes a thick mud. He uses a screen to remove most of the | 60–72 |
| rocks from the dirt so the bricks are smoother. Next, he | 73–83 |
| adds some straw to the mud. The straw helps the bricks hold | 84–95 |
| together better. | 96–97 |
| When the adobe mixture looks just right, Mr. Jones pours it | 98–108 |
| into some wooden molds. The mud stays in the molds drying in | 109–120 |
| the sun for days until it has hardened. Then Mr. Jones removes | 121–132 |
| the bricks from the molds. | 133–137 |
| He builds the wall by stacking the bricks on top of each | 138–149 |
| other in level rows. He puts adobe mud between the bricks to | 150–161 |
| hold them in place. Later he will paint the wall with whitewash. | 162–173 |

---

**EVALUATING CODES
FOR ORAL FLUENCY**

sky            (/) words read incorrectly

blue
 ^  sky      (^) inserted word
                  ( ] ) after the last word

---

**READING RATE AND ACCURACY**

Total Words Read:  _____

Number of Errors:  _____

Number of Correct Words
Read Per Minute (WPM):  _____

Accuracy Rate:  _____

(Number of Correct Words Read per
Minute ÷ Total Words Read)

---

**READING FLUENCY**

| | Low | Average | High |
|---|---|---|---|
| Decoding ability | ○ | ○ | ○ |
| Pace | ○ | ○ | ○ |
| Syntax | ○ | ○ | ○ |
| Self-correction | ○ | ○ | ○ |
| Intonation | ○ | ○ | ○ |

---

**Record student rates on the Oral Fluency Scores pages.**

Name _____ Date _____ Score _____

# Energy Makes Things Happen

## Vocabulary

**Read each item. Fill in the bubble for the answer you think is correct.**

1. Something that is **stored** is
   - Ⓐ eaten.
   - Ⓑ loose.
   - Ⓒ used often.
   - Ⓓ put away.

2. Which Latin root means "mind"?
   - Ⓐ *sol*
   - Ⓑ *mem*
   - Ⓒ *vid*
   - Ⓓ *trib*

3. Both heat and light are kinds of **energy.** In this sentence, **energy** means
   - Ⓐ the power to do work.
   - Ⓑ things that are used every day.
   - Ⓒ things that are easy to see.
   - Ⓓ things that cost a lot of money.

4. Wood can **release** gases as it is burned. When you **release** something, you
   - Ⓐ run with it.
   - Ⓑ bury it.
   - Ⓒ read it carefully.
   - Ⓓ let it loose.

5. A rock on the top of a hill will roll back down the hill **eventually.** This means the rock will roll down the hill
   - Ⓐ quickly.
   - Ⓑ only in the wintertime.
   - Ⓒ sooner or later.
   - Ⓓ when it loses size.

**Energy Makes Things Happen** (continued)

## Comprehension

Read the following questions carefully. Then completely fill in the bubble of each correct answer. You may look back at the selection to find the answer to each of the questions.

1. Most of our energy comes from
   Ⓐ fossil fuels.
   🅑 the sun.
   Ⓒ rocks.
   Ⓓ trees.

2. What kind of energy is in a carrot?
   Ⓐ heat energy
   Ⓑ light energy
   Ⓒ moving energy
   🅓 stored energy

## Energy Makes Things Happen (continued)

3. What happens after a rock on a hill is given a little push?

   Ⓐ It does not move because rocks have no energy.

   Ⓑ It rolls down the hill part of the way.

   Ⓒ It rolls all the way down the hill.

   Ⓓ It moves farther up the hill.

4. Which of these happens first?

   Ⓐ A cow eats grass.

   Ⓑ You drink a glass of milk.

   Ⓒ You hit a home run playing baseball.

   Ⓓ The sun hits a blade of grass.

5. Why did the author write the selection?

   Ⓐ to show how all energy comes from the sun

   Ⓑ to help readers make up experiments about energy

   Ⓒ to tell the rules of baseball

   Ⓓ to show that different rocks have different kinds of energy

**Energy Makes Things Happen** (continued)

**Read the following questions carefully. Use complete sentences to answer the questions.** Possible answers below

6. What is wind?

Wind is air that moves or air that has energy.

7. What happens when a girl swings a bat and hits a ball?

Energy is transferred from her arms, through the bat and to the ball.

8. How is energy in a rock on top of a hill the same as energy in a carrot?

Both a rock on top of a hill and a carrot have stored energy.

9. Why does the author suggest the use of toy cars?

The author makes this suggestion to give us a simple visual example about the transfer of energy.

10. Why are the cars in the experiment on a hard surface?

They are on a hard surface so that most of the energy is transferred.

## Energy Makes Things Happen (continued)

**Read the question below. Write complete sentences for your answer. Support your answer with information from the selection.**

**Linking to the Concepts** Does energy ever go away? Explain your answer.

_____

_____

_____

_____

_____

**Read the question below. Your answer should be based on your own experience. Write complete sentences for your answer.**

**Personal Response** What do you do that requires a lot of energy? Write about what it is and why it uses up so much energy.

_____

_____

_____

_____

**Energy Makes Things Happen** (continued)

## Grammar, Usage, and Mechanics

**Read each question. Fill in the bubble beside the answer in each group that is correct. If none of the answers is correct, choose the last answer, "none of the above."**

**1.** Which sentence has correct punctuation?

Ⓐ Nam said, "I'll vote."  Ⓒ Nam said, I'll vote.

Ⓑ "Nam said, I'll vote".  Ⓓ none of the above

**2.** Which sentence has correct punctuation?

Ⓐ "We should buy a gift for Ms. Hayes" Eileen suggested.

Ⓑ "We should buy a gift for Ms. Hayes," Eileen suggested.

Ⓒ "We should buy a gift for Ms. Hayes", Eileen suggested.

Ⓓ none of the above

**3.** Which sentence has correct punctuation?

Ⓐ Do you like to play basketball.

Ⓑ Five players are on each team!

Ⓒ Would you like to go to the park to play?

Ⓓ none of the above

**4.** Which sentence has correct punctuation?

Ⓐ The town is tiny it has just a post office; and a store.

Ⓑ The town is tiny; it has just a post office and a store.

Ⓒ The town is tiny it has; just a post office and a store.

Ⓓ none of the above

**5.** Which sentence has correct punctuation?

Ⓐ The family had three: pets, a dog, a cat, and a parakeet.

Ⓑ The family: had three pets a dog, a cat, and a parakeet.

Ⓒ The family had three pets: a dog, a cat, and a parakeet.

Ⓓ none of the above

**Energy Makes Things Happen** (continued)

## Analyzing the Selection

**Read the prompt below. Write complete sentences for your summary.**

Write a summary of the selection "Energy Makes Things Happen." Be sure to include the most important ideas from the selection.

_____

_____

_____

_____

_____

_____

_____

_____

_____

_____

_____

_____

_____

_____

## Energy Makes Things Happen (continued)

## Oral Fluency Assessment

### *Living in the White House*

| | |
|---|---|
| Most people think of the White House as a building where | 1–11 |
| the president works. But it is also the home for the president. | 12–23 |
| If the walls could talk, they could tell many interesting stories. | 24–34 |
| Teddy Roosevelt had six children. They were active children. | 35–43 |
| Back then, the family's rooms and offices were in the same part | 44–55 |
| of the White House. | 56–59 |
| The boys ran in and out of the rooms. They played games. | 60–71 |
| They had pillow fights with their father. They skated in the | 72–82 |
| halls. They walked on stilts. They would sneak up on and scare | 83–94 |
| people who were working. | 95–98 |
| Once when one of the boys was sick, his brothers brought | 99–109 |
| his pony to him. They hoped the visitor would cheer him up. | 110–121 |
| Another time, one of the boys cut a baseball diamond in the | 122–133 |
| White House lawn. | 134–136 |
| The President liked playing with his children, but he needed | 137–146 |
| a place to work. He built the West Wing. That way, the offices | 147–159 |
| were away from the family area. This was better for the | 160–170 |
| presidents' families and for their staffs. | 171–176 |

**EVALUATING CODES FOR ORAL FLUENCY**

sky (/) words read incorrectly

blue
^ sky (^) inserted word
( ] ) after the last word

**READING RATE AND ACCURACY**

Total Words Read: _____

Number of Errors: _____

Number of Correct Words
Read Per Minute (WPM): _____

Accuracy Rate: _____

(Number of Correct Words Read per
Minute ÷ Total Words Read)

**READING FLUENCY**

| | Low | Average | High |
|---|---|---|---|
| Decoding ability | ○ | ○ | ○ |
| Pace | ○ | ○ | ○ |
| Syntax | ○ | ○ | ○ |
| Self-correction | ○ | ○ | ○ |
| Intonation | ○ | ○ | ○ |

**Record student rates on the Oral Fluency Scores pages.**

Name _____ Date _____ Score _____

# Who Eats What? Food Chains and Food Webs

## Vocabulary

**Read each item. Fill in the bubble for the answer you think is correct.**

**1.** If you **depend** on something, you

Ⓐ show it.        Ⓒ buy it.

🅑 need it.        Ⓓ build it.

**2.** A synonym for **linked** is

Ⓐ straight.        Ⓒ connected.

Ⓑ crooked.        Ⓓ important.

**3.** You need a **microscope** to see some of the plants in the water. A **microscope** is

Ⓐ a small, fast boat.

Ⓑ a large glass container.

Ⓒ a tool for looking at tiny things.

Ⓓ a small pointed pair of tweezers.

**4.** Otters live in beds of giant **seaweed.** What is **seaweed?**

Ⓐ a plant that grows in the sea

Ⓑ leaves and twigs floating on the sea

Ⓒ a smooth rock

Ⓓ a leafy tree near the sea

**5.** We are in a **slightly** longer food chain than cows. In this sentence, **slightly** means

Ⓐ very much.        Ⓒ oddly.

🅓 beautifully.        🅓 just a little bit.

## Who Eats What? Food Chains and Food Webs (continued)

## Comprehension

**Read the following questions carefully. Then completely fill in the bubble of each correct answer. You may look back at the selection to find the answer to each of the questions.**

1. According to the selection, green plants are the only living things

   Ⓐ  that hawks eat.

   Ⓑ  that are at the top of the food chain.

   Ⓒ  that depend on the sun.

   Ⓓ  that make their own food.

2. Which of these is closest to the top of its food chain?

   Ⓐ  a caterpillar

   **Ⓑ  a hawk**

   Ⓒ  a wren

   Ⓓ  a leaf

## Who Eats What? Food Chains and Food Webs (continued)

**3.** What happened right after humans killed nearly all the Pacific sea otters?

   Ⓐ Kelp began to disappear.

   Ⓑ Eagles appeared in large numbers.

   Ⓒ Sea urchins disappeared.

   Ⓓ Fishermen caught all of the fish.

**4.** All food chains begin with

   Ⓐ very small animals.

   Ⓑ something nobody else eats.

   Ⓒ green plants.

   Ⓓ an apple tree.

**5.** A fact about Antarctica is

   Ⓐ that it is very beautiful.

   Ⓑ that people do not like to visit there.

   Ⓒ that plants and animals live there.

   Ⓓ that it is too far away to visit.

**Who Eats What? Food Chains and Food Webs** (continued)

**Read the following questions carefully. Use complete sentences to answer the questions.** Possible answers below

**6.** What is the difference between a food chain and a food web?

A food web is made up of many food chains.

**7.** What caused the kelp to disappear?

There were no otters to eat. The sea urchins cut off the stems of the kelp.

**8.** Why would corn be important to a cat?

Mice eat corn, and cats eat mice. Without corn, the cat would lose a source of food.

**9.** How is a food chain in the sea different from a food chain on land?

Food chains in the sea are longer and more difficult to study.

**10.** Why did the author write this selection?

The author wrote this selection to show how living things depend on each other.

## Who Eats What? Food Chains and Food Webs (continued)

**Read the question below. Write complete sentences for your answer. Support your answer with information from the selection.**

**Linking to the Concepts** Why do we need to care for and protect Earth?

_____

_____

_____

_____

_____

**Read the question below. Your answer should be based on your own experience. Write complete sentences for your answer.**

**Personal Response** What have you done that ended up having multiple effects? Identify the action and the results.

_____

_____

_____

_____

_____

_____

## Who Eats What? Food Chains and Food Webs (continued)

## Grammar, Usage, and Mechanics

**Fill in the bubble beside the answer that is correct.**

**1.** Which of these is a compound sentence?

Ⓐ John, who is in fifth grade, went with our class.

Ⓑ The dog chased its toy down the stairs.

Ⓒ It snowed last night, so we went sledding in the morning.

Ⓓ none of the above

**2.** Which sentence has a compound subject?

Ⓐ A noise frightened the deer and her fawn.

Ⓑ The deer and the fawn reached the creek.

Ⓒ The deer jumped, but the fawn walked.

Ⓓ none of the above

**3.** What is the best way to combine these two sentences?

**A group of students sang. Their parents sang, also.**

Ⓐ A group of students sang, their parents also sang.

Ⓑ Parents sang a group of students did, also.

Ⓒ A group of students and their parents sang.

Ⓓ none of the above

**4.** Which sentence has correct punctuation?

Ⓐ Maren packed a sandwich fruit and a drink for lunch.

Ⓑ Maren packed a sandwich, fruit, and a drink for lunch.

Ⓒ Maren packed a sandwich, fruit, and a drink, for lunch.

Ⓓ none of the above

**5.** Which list has a mistake in punctuation?

Ⓐ a pen pencil, and paper.    Ⓒ the chair, desk, and table.

Ⓑ a door, a window, and a closet    Ⓓ none of the above

**Who Eats What? Food Chains and Food Webs** (continued)

## Analyzing the Selection

**Read the question below. Write complete sentences for your answer. Support your answer with information from the selections.**

Think about the selection "The Snowflake: A Water Cycle Story." How is that selection similar to "Who Eats What? Food Chains and Food Webs"?

_____

_____

_____

_____

_____

_____

_____

_____

_____

_____

_____

_____

## Who Eats What? Food Chains and Food Webs (continued)

## Oral Fluency Assessment

### *The Cheetah*

| | |
|---|---|
| Adult cheetahs can weigh nearly two hundred pounds. They | 1–9 |
| can run close to seventy miles per hour. They are considered | 10–20 |
| the fastest animals on land. | 21–25 |
| This pretty cat has long legs. Its fur is yellow-brown, and it | 26–38 |
| has small black spots. Cheetahs live in Africa and Asia. They | 39–49 |
| are found in many zoos in this country. | 50–57 |
| Cheetahs are hunters who chase and kill other animals for | 58–67 |
| food. They can be trapped and tamed, but they do not make | 68–79 |
| good pets. The cheetah has claws like a house cat, but there is | 80–92 |
| a difference. The house cat can draw in its claws so it does not | 93–106 |
| scratch. The cheetah can not draw in its claws all the way. It | 107–119 |
| would tear up your home if it visited. | 120–127 |
| Some other members of the cat family are the lion and | 128–138 |
| the tiger. The cougar and the lynx are also in the cat family. | 139–151 |
| All these cats are hunters and meat eaters. They have sharp | 152–162 |
| claws and teeth. The jaguar, the leopard, and the cheetah all | 163–173 |
| have spots. But no other member of the cat family is as fast as | 174–187 |
| the cheetah. | 188–189 |

**EVALUATING CODES FOR ORAL FLUENCY**

sky      (/) words read incorrectly

blue
^   sky    (^) inserted word
        ( ] ) after the last word

**READING RATE AND ACCURACY**

Total Words Read: _____

Number of Errors: _____

Number of Correct Words Read Per Minute (WPM): _____

Accuracy Rate: _____

(Number of Correct Words Read per Minute ÷ Total Words Read)

**READING FLUENCY**

| | Low | Average | High |
|---|---|---|---|
| Decoding ability | ○ | ○ | ○ |
| Pace | ○ | ○ | ○ |
| Syntax | ○ | ○ | ○ |
| Self-correction | ○ | ○ | ○ |
| Intonation | ○ | ○ | ○ |

Record student rates on the Oral Fluency Scores pages.

Name _____ Date _____ Score _____

# What Rot! Nature's Mighty Recycler

## Vocabulary

**Read each item. Fill in the bubble for the answer you think is correct.**

**1.** A **burrow** is a type of

  (A) hole.  (C) tree.

  (B) food.  (D) animal.

**2.** An antonym for **droop** is

  (A) curl.  (C) rise.

  (B) rush.  (D) sink.

**3.** Rot makes an apple **shrivel** up. This means that the apple

  (A) falls off of the tree.

  (B) is ready for cooking.

  (C) becomes more flavorful.

  (D) becomes wrinkled and small.

**4.** Earthworms tunnel through soil so that air and water can **circulate.** In this sentence, **circulate** means

  (A) come from the sky.

  (B) become trapped in gaps.

  (C) flow around freely.

  (D) get taken in by plants.

**5.** A shrew can be caught by a **predator.** A **predator** is

  (A) an animal that eats only plants.

  (B) an animal that hunts other animals for food.

  (C) a type of spider's web.

  (D) an old tree that has sticky vines.

**What Rot! Nature's Mighty Recycler** (continued)

## Comprehension

**Read the following questions carefully. Then completely fill in the bubble of each correct answer. You may look back at the selection to find the answer to each of the questions.**

**1.** What does the mold on the pumpkin look like?

Ⓐ a happy grin

Ⓑ moss

Ⓒ blue chicken pox

Ⓓ a balloon which has burst

**2.** Which of these is not a rotter?

Ⓐ bacteria

Ⓑ insects

Ⓒ soil

Ⓓ animals

UNIT
2

**Lesson 4**

## What Rot! Nature's Mighty Recycler (continued)

**3.** Why does the tree in the selection fall?

Ⓐ It is chopped down.

Ⓑ It has a core that became rotten.

Ⓒ It was blown over by the wind.

Ⓓ It was pushed over by a large animal.

**4.** What happens after the ichneumon wasp lays its eggs?

Ⓐ Ants make tunnels in the log.

Ⓑ The tree falls over.

Ⓒ A chipmunk burrows under the tree's roots.

Ⓓ The wasp larvae eat the insect larvae.

**5.** Which of these is an opinion about rot?

Ⓐ Rot is a mighty force.

Ⓑ Rotters are mostly animals and plants.

Ⓒ Everything eats something else.

Ⓓ Rot is part of the cycle of life.

**What Rot! Nature's Mighty Recycler** (continued)

**Read the following questions carefully. Use complete sentences to answer the questions.** Possible answers below

6. What would happens if things did not rot?

   Dead things would pile up and could smother the earth.

7. Why does a rotter go to a dying tree?

   All living things need food and shelter; they are found in a dying tree.

8. What eventually happens to the log in the selection?

   The log eventually becomes part of the soil.

9. To what type of clock does the author compare the cycle of life?

   The cycle of life is like a clock that never stops.

10. What happens in the springtime?

    In the spring, the cycle of life begins again.

## What Rot! Nature's Mighty Recycler (continued)

**Read the question below. Write complete sentences for your answer. Support your answer with information from the selection.**

**Linking to the Concepts** Why do some people have compost piles?

_____

_____

_____

_____

_____

**Read the question below. Your answer should be based on your own experience. Write complete sentences for your answer.**

**Personal Response** Did this selection cause you to think differently about the world around you? Explain your answer.

_____

_____

_____

_____

_____

_____

**What Rot! Nature's Mighty Recycler** (continued)

## Grammar, Usage, and Mechanics

**Fill in the bubble beside the answer that is correct.**

1. Which sentence has a compound predicate?

   Ⓐ Students often fish in the pond, which is near the school.

   ⬤Ⓑ Pat fishes each morning and swims every night.

   Ⓒ Lynn took lessons, and now Jim wants to learn.

   Ⓓ none of the above

2. What is the best way to combine these two sentences?
   **Squirrels live in those trees. They build nests near the top.**

   ⬤Ⓐ Squirrels live in those trees and build nests near the top.

   Ⓑ Squirrels build nests near the top of those trees.

   Ⓒ Squirrels live in those trees and; they build nests.

   Ⓓ none of the above

3. Which of these has a compound subject?

   Ⓐ Firefighters used hoses when they reached the building.

   ⬤Ⓑ Flames and smoke could be seen for miles and miles.

   Ⓒ The fire lasted an hour, and the building was ruined.

   Ⓓ none of the above

4. Which sentence has correct punctuation?

   Ⓐ Mom rakes her garden?

   Ⓑ She likes us to help her pull weeds!

   Ⓒ After we pick vegetables, Grandma cans some.

   Ⓓ none of the above

5. Which of these is an imperative sentence?

   Ⓐ What time is it?          Ⓒ Hand me that.

   Ⓑ Look out!                 Ⓓ none of the above

**What Rot! Nature's Mighty Recycler** (continued)

## Analyzing the Selection

**Read the questions below. Write complete sentences for your answer. Support your answer with information from the selection.**

How does the author show the importance of rotting on the environment? How is the author successful in making the reader understand this importance?

_____

_____

_____

_____

_____

_____

_____

_____

_____

_____

_____

## What Rot! Nature's Mighty Recycler (continued)

## Oral Fluency Assessment

### *Smoke Signals*

| | |
|---|---|
| How do you talk to someone who is far away? Today | 1–11 |
| communication over long distances is not hard. But it was not | 12–22 |
| so simple for the Plains Indians. They came up with a smart | 23–34 |
| method to do it, though. They used smoke signals. | 35–43 |
| They did not use these signals to say things like "How are | 44–55 |
| you?" They used smoke signals like a code. The code told other | 56–67 |
| tribes when there was game in the area. Signals were good for | 68–79 |
| warning others that enemies were coming, too. | 80–86 |
| Making smoke signals took a lot more than a strong fire. | 87–97 |
| Plains Indians built their fires in a specific way. They used | 98–108 |
| damp grass or green leaves. These things make a lot of smoke. | 109–120 |
| They used certain wood or leaves to make colored smoke. Then | 121–131 |
| they laid a blanket over the fire. When they lifted it up, puffs of | 132–145 |
| smoke of different sizes came out. Smoke signals could be seen | 146–156 |
| from very far away. | 157–160 |
| Today few people still know how to make smoke signals or | 161–171 |
| to understand their meanings. But it was once a fast and useful | 172–183 |
| way to communicate in the West. | 184–189 |

---

**EVALUATING CODES
FOR ORAL FLUENCY**

sky      (/) words read incorrectly

blue
^   sky    (^) inserted word
          ( ] ) after the last word

---

**READING RATE AND ACCURACY**

Total Words Read:      _____

Number of Errors:      _____

Number of Correct Words
Read Per Minute (WPM):      _____

Accuracy Rate:      _____

(Number of Correct Words Read per
Minute ÷ Total Words Read)

---

**READING FLUENCY**

| | Low | Average | High |
|---|---|---|---|
| Decoding ability | ○ | ○ | ○ |
| Pace | ○ | ○ | ○ |
| Syntax | ○ | ○ | ○ |
| Self-correction | ○ | ○ | ○ |
| Intonation | ○ | ○ | ○ |

**Record student rates on the Oral Fluency Scores pages.**

Name _____ Date _____ Score _____

# The Great Kapok Tree

**Vocabulary**

**Read each item. Fill in the bubble for the answer you think is correct.**

1. Something that is **smoldering** is
   - (A) burning.
   - (B) boiling.
   - (C) rolling.
   - (D) flaming.

2. What does the Latin root **form,** as in *formation,* mean?
   - (A) sound
   - (B) city
   - (C) measure
   - (D) shape

3. The snake tells the man that **ancestors** have lived in the tree. Ancestors are
   - (A) animals with long tails.
   - (B) birds that make big nests.
   - (C) relatives from long ago.
   - (D) plants that grow quickly.

4. The porcupines tell the man that the kapok tree makes **oxygen. Oxygen** is
   - (A) a beautiful flower.
   - (B) an edible leaf.
   - (C) a tasty fruit.
   - (D) a gas we breathe.

5. The man awoke with a **start.** This means
   - (A) he jumped from surprise.
   - (B) he woke up next to a small animal.
   - (C) he heard a loud sound as he awoke.
   - (D) he woke up and had to start working.

**The Great Kapok Tree** (continued)

## Comprehension

**Read the following questions carefully. Then completely fill in the bubble of each correct answer. You may look back at the selection to find the answer to each of the questions.**

**1.** All of these are reasons given for the man falling asleep EXCEPT

Ⓐ he got tired while chopping the tree.

Ⓑ the hot day made him tired.

Ⓒ the hum of the forest lulled him to sleep.

Ⓓ he had eaten a large meal.

**2.** Which of these visits the sleeping man first?

Ⓐ a child

Ⓑ a snake

Ⓒ a toucan

Ⓓ porcupines

**The Great Kapok Tree** (continued)

3. The author wrote this selection to

   (A) show us how to take care of trees.

   (B) make sure we are chopping down some other type of tree.

   (C) show that what people do affects the whole world.

   (D) let us know that animals really can talk to humans.

4. At the end of the selection, the man leaves the forest

   (A) after chopping down the tree.

   (B) without chopping down the tree.

   (C) with the snake.

   (D) and meets up with the other man.

5. How is the snake like the bee?

   (A) both live in the tree

   (B) both hiss

   (C) both pollinate trees and flowers

   (D) both buzz

**The Great Kapok Tree** (continued)

**Read the following questions carefully. Use complete sentences to answer the questions.** Possible answers below

**6.** Why does the forest become quiet when the men enter it?

The creatures in the forest stop making noise and watch them.

**7.** Name some of the animals that visit the man while he sleeps.

A boa constrictor, birds, a jaguar, and others.

**8.** What will happen to the jaguar if the Kapok tree is chopped down?

He might go hungry if it is chopped down.

**9.** How can a forest disappear if someone chops down one tree?

Other people might think it is okay for them to do so as well.

**10.** How have the animals helped the man?

They have helped him see the importance of the rain forest.

**The Great Kapok Tree** (continued)

Read the question below. Write complete sentences for your answer. Support your answer with information from the selection.

**Linking to the Concepts** What is the effect when just one small part of the cycle of life is removed?

_____

_____

_____

_____

Read the question below. Your answer should be based on your own experience. Write complete sentences for your answer.

**Personal Response** How does this selection make you feel about the place of people in the cycle of life? Explain why you feel this way.

_____

_____

_____

_____

_____

**The Great Kapok Tree** (continued)

## Grammar, Usage, and Mechanics

**Fill in the bubble beside the answer that is correct.**

**1.** Which sentence has correct punctuation?

Ⓐ Ryan is our top wrestler; he is going to the state meet.

Ⓑ Ryan is our top wrestler, he is going to the state meet.

Ⓒ Ryan is our top wrestler he is going to the state meet.

Ⓓ none of the above

**2.** Which sentence has correct punctuation?

Ⓐ The fox darted across the road a driver stopped to look.

Ⓑ The fox darted across the road a driver, stopped to look.

Ⓒ The fox darted across; the road a driver stopped to look.

Ⓓ none of the above

**3.** Which sentence is incorrect?

Ⓐ Ari painted two pictures; one of them won a medal.

Ⓑ A reporter showed up Ari's parents were surprised.

Ⓒ Ari takes special lessons.

Ⓓ none of the above

**4.** What is the best way to combine these two sentences?
**Peter studies art. Anne studies finance.**

Ⓐ Peter studies art so Anne studies finance.

Ⓑ Peter studies art Anne studies finance.

Ⓒ Peter studies art, but Anne studies finance.

Ⓓ none of the above

**5.** What sentences is incorrect?

Ⓐ The fly came near; and the frog caught it.

Ⓑ The fly came near and the frog caught it.

Ⓒ The fly came near, and the frog caught it.

Ⓓ none of the above

**The Great Kapok Tree** (continued)

## Analyzing the Selection

**Read the questions below. Write complete sentences for your answer. Support your answer with information from the selections.**

What are some of the important ideas you learned about cycles and chains in this unit? Why are these ideas important to you? Should they be important to other people?

_____

_____

_____

_____

_____

_____

_____

_____

_____

_____

_____

_____

_____

## The Great Kapok Tree (continued)

# Oral Fluency Assessment

### *The Siberian Tiger*

The shy Siberian tiger lives in the wild areas of Asia. It is one          1–14
of the rarest big cats in the world. There are only five hundred           15–27
or so wild tigers left. People are worried that if we do not do            28–41
something soon, this beautiful animal will be gone forever.                42–50

An adult tiger will grow to be more than six hundred pounds.               51–62
In many ways, they are like jungle cats. But they are different            63–74
from other tigers in one way. Their stripes are brown, not black.          75–86

Siberian tigers roam the forests. They hunt deer, wild boar,               87–96
and rabbits. Sometimes they eat fish such as salmon. But they              97–107
find deer to be the best meal.                                             108–114

Most of these tigers live in zoos across the world. Some                   115–125
people think that these captive tigers should be released back             126–135
into the wild. That sounds like a great idea, at first. But it is not.     136–150
Tigers in a zoo do not know how to hunt for food. They would               151–164
starve in the wild. So for now, zoos will continue to raise these          165–177
rare and lovely creatures.                                                 178–181

### EVALUATING CODES FOR ORAL FLUENCY

sky          (/) words read incorrectly

blue
^   sky      (^) inserted word
             ( ] ) after the last word

### READING RATE AND ACCURACY

Total Words Read:  _____

Number of Errors:  _____

Number of Correct Words
Read Per Minute (WPM):  _____

Accuracy Rate:  _____

(Number of Correct Words Read per
Minute ÷ Total Words Read)

### READING FLUENCY

|                  | Low | Average | High |
|------------------|-----|---------|------|
| Decoding ability | O   | O       | O    |
| Pace             | O   | O       | O    |
| Syntax           | O   | O       | O    |
| Self-correction  | O   | O       | O    |
| Intonation       | O   | O       | O    |

**Record student rates on the Oral Fluency Scores pages.**

Name _____ Date _____ Score _____

# Expository Writing

## Writing Situation
Energy use in your life

## Audience
Your friends and family

## Directions for Writing
People use energy every day. Write about the energy you use. Think about everything you do, from riding in a car or bus in the morning to reading by lamplight before you go to bed. If you are able, explain to readers where the energy you use comes from.

## Checklist
You will earn the best score if you
- think about your ideas and plan your writing before you begin.
- include several different ways you use energy.
- write so that readers will connect their experiences to your energy use.
- write paragraphs that have a topic sentence and focus on related ideas.
- use transition words to go from one idea to another.
- vary your sentences and the words you use.
- write more sentences and longer sentences when you revise.
- use correct capitalization, punctuation, and spelling.
- use subjects, verbs, and modifiers correctly.
- choose words that mean what you want to say.

# Four Point Rubrics for Expository Writing

| Genre | 1 Point | 2 Points | 3 Points | 4 Points |
|---|---|---|---|---|
| **Expository** | Composition has no introduction or clear topic. It offers a group of loosely related facts or a series of poorly written steps. No conclusion is included. | Composition is clearly organized around main points with supportive facts or assertions. Composition has no clear introduction, but its topic is identifiable. However, it includes many facts unrelated to the topic, or it describes things in a disorganized way. No conclusion is included. | Main points and supportive details can be identified, but they are not clearly marked. Composition has an introduction and offers facts about the topic. Some facts may be irrelevant, or some ideas may be vague or out of order. The report is fairly well organized but doesn't have a strong conclusion. | Traces and constructs a line of argument, identifying part-to-whole relations. Main points are supported with logical and appropriate evidence. Composition begins with an introduction and offers relevant facts about the topic or describes the topic appropriately. The report is organized using cause/effect, comparison/contrast, or another pattern. It ends with a strong conclusion. |

## Writing Traits

| | 1 Point | 2 Points | 3 Points | 4 Points |
|---|---|---|---|---|
| **Focus** | Topic is unclear or wanders and must be inferred. Extraneous material may be present. | Topic/position/direction is unclear and must be inferred. | Topic/position is stated and previewed and maintained. Mainly stays on topic. | Topic/position is clearly stated, previewed, and maintained throughout the paper. Topics and details are tied together with a central theme or purpose that is maintained /threaded throughout the paper. |
| **Ideas/Content** | Superficial and/or minimal content is included. | Main ideas are understandable, although they may be overly broad or simplistic, and the results may not be effective. Supporting detail is limited, insubstantial, overly general or off topic. | The writing is clear and focused. The reader can easily understand the main ideas. Support is present, although it may be limited or rather general. | Writing is exceptionally clear, focused, and interesting. Main ideas stand out and are developed by strong support and rich details. |
| **Elaboration (supporting details and examples that develop the main idea)** | States ideas or points with minimal detail to support them. | Includes sketchy, redundant, or general details; some may be irrelevant. Support for key ideas is very uneven. | Includes mix of general statements and specific details/examples. Support is mostly relevant but may be uneven and lack depth in places. | Includes specific details and supporting examples for each key point/idea. May use compare/contrast to support. |

## Writing Conventions

| | 1 Point | 2 Points | 3 Points | 4 Points |
|---|---|---|---|---|
| **Conventions Overall** | Numerous errors in usage, grammar, spelling, capitalization, and punctuation repeatedly distract the reader and make the text difficult to read. The reader finds it difficult to focus on the message. | The writing demonstrates limited control of standard writing conventions (punctuation, spelling, capitalization, grammar, and usage). Errors sometimes impede readability. | The writing demonstrates control of standard writing conventions (punctuation, spelling, capitalization, grammar, and usage). Minor errors, while perhaps noticeable, do not impede readability. | The writing demonstrates exceptionally strong control of standard writing conventions (punctuation, spelling, capitalization, grammar, and usage) and uses them effectively to enhance communication. Errors are so few and so minor that the reader can easily skim over them. |

**UNIT 3** — **Lesson 1**

Name _____ Date _____ Score _____

# The U.S. Constitution and You

## Vocabulary

**Read each item. Fill in the bubble for the answer you think is correct.**

**1.** Which word contains the Greek root meaning "people"?

  Ⓐ dialog      Ⓒ democracy

  Ⓑ generation      Ⓓ phonics

**2.** Another word for **declared** is

  Ⓐ asked.      Ⓒ clarified.

  Ⓑ supplied.      Ⓓ announced.

**3.** The states could not be forced to **contribute** to the United States. This means that the states did not have to

  Ⓐ give money or time.

  Ⓑ join other states to make the new country.

  Ⓒ change their laws.

  Ⓓ elect representatives.

**4.** The Supreme Court decides which laws are **proper** under the Constitution. Laws that are **proper** are

  Ⓐ suitable.

  Ⓑ difficult to understand.

  Ⓒ easy to follow.

  Ⓓ memorable.

**5.** The first league of states did not have the power to **settle** disputes between states. **Settle** means about the same as

  Ⓐ create.      Ⓒ understand.

  Ⓑ decide.      Ⓓ explain.

**The U.S. Constitution and You** (continued)

## Comprehension

Read the following questions carefully. Then completely fill in the bubble of each correct answer. You may look back at the selection to find the answer to each of the questions.

**1.** When was the Constitution written?

Ⓐ 1776

Ⓑ 1783

Ⓒ 1787

Ⓓ 1812

**2.** Which state did not send a representative to Philadelphia to help write the Constitution?

Ⓐ Rhode Island

Ⓑ Massachusetts

Ⓒ Connecticut

Ⓓ New York

**The U.S. Constitution and You** (continued)

3. What is the job of Congress?

   Ⓐ  to veto laws

   Ⓑ  to interpret laws

   Ⓒ  to carry out laws

   Ⓓ  to make laws

4. Courts can do all of these things EXCEPT

   Ⓐ  appoint U.S. judges.

   Ⓑ  settle disagreements about the law.

   Ⓒ  explain what the law means.

   Ⓓ  punish people who disobey the law.

5. What does the author identify as a responsibility of the citizenship?

   Ⓐ  using paper currency

   Ⓑ  voting for president

   Ⓒ  vetoing laws

   Ⓓ  choosing judges

**The U.S. Constitution and You** (continued)

**Read the following questions carefully. Use complete sentences to answer the questions.** Possible answers below

6. Based on what you read in the selection, what conclusion can you draw about the Articles of Confederation?

The Articles of Confederation did not account for a growing country.

7. What were some of the problems with the Articles of Confederation?

It had no real rules about types of money or for raising money.

8. What is the difference between a monarchy and a democracy?

A monarchy has one person in control; a democracy listens to the people.

9. Why are there three branches of government?

The three branches divide up the work of running the country.

10. Why are the constitutions of other countries modeled after ours?

It has been successful for such a long time that others want to imitate it.

## The U.S. Constitution and You (continued)

**Read the question below. Write complete sentences for your answer. Support your answer with information from the selection.**

**Linking to the Concepts** How has the Constitution helped the United States become a great nation?

_____

_____

_____

_____

_____

**Read the question below. Your answer should be based on your own experience. Write complete sentences for your answer.**

**Personal Response** How is your life impacted by the Constitution?

_____

_____

_____

_____

_____

## The U.S. Constitution and You (continued)

## Grammar, Usage, and Mechanics

**Read each question. Fill in the bubble beside the answer in each group that is correct. If none of the answers is correct, choose the last answer, "none of the above."**

1. Which pronoun can take the place of the underlined part in this sentence?

   **The coach asked <u>Jim and Matt</u> to come to practice early.**

   Ⓐ they      Ⓒ themselves

   🅑 them      Ⓓ none of the above

2. Which pronoun can take the place of the underlined part in this sentence?

   **When did <u>Marge</u> finish the science project?**

   Ⓐ herself      Ⓒ she

   Ⓑ her      Ⓓ none of the above

3. Which sentence has correct punctuation?

   🅐 One poodle's coat is gray.      Ⓒ One poodles' coat is gray.

   Ⓑ One poodles coat is gray.      Ⓓ none of the above

4. Which sentence has correct punctuation?

   Ⓐ All the horse's bridle's were made of leather.

   Ⓑ All the horses's bridles were made of leather.

   Ⓒ All the horses bridles were made of leather.

   🅓 none of the above

5. Which sentence has correct punctuation?

   🅐 The puppies' paws were covered with mud.

   Ⓑ The puppies's paws were covered with mud.

   Ⓒ The puppie's paws were covered with mud.

   Ⓓ none of the above

**The U.S. Constitution and You** (continued)

## Analyzing the Selection

**Read the question below. Write complete sentences for your response. Support your answer with information from the selection.**

Do you think the framers of the Constitution would recognize their handiwork in the current United States? Use information from the selection as well as your own opinion.

_____

_____

_____

_____

_____

_____

_____

_____

_____

_____

_____

_____

## The U.S. Constitution and You (continued)

## Oral Fluency Assessment

### *Tornado!*

The rain pounds down. The sky turns a strange color. A          1–11
sound like a roaring train gets louder. A tornado is coming!     12–22
Tornadoes can hit at any time. However, they are most            23–32
common in the spring and summer. May and June are the worst      33–44
months of all.                                                   45–47
A tornado forms when warm air rises and passes through           48–57
cooler air. The rising warm air creates something called an      58–67
updraft. The warm air gets high in the atmosphere. Then it       68–78
cools off. It sinks back down. This is a downdraft.              79–88
A tornado gains its strength through a special type of storm.    89–99
This storm is called a supercell. These storms are filled with   100–110
energy. All this energy makes the updrafts very powerful. Then   111–120
the air starts to spin. A tornado is on the loose!               121–131
Some tornadoes are small. Others are huge. These storms          132–140
can rip through a town and destroy all they find in their paths. 141–153
More than one thousand tornadoes are reported each year          154–162
in the United States. Almost all of them occur in the flat middle 163–175
part of the country. This area is known as "Tornado Alley."      176–186

---

**EVALUATING CODES
FOR ORAL FLUENCY**

sky          (/) words read incorrectly

blue
^   sky    (^) inserted word
            ( ] ) after the last word

---

**READING RATE AND ACCURACY**

Total Words Read:  _____

Number of Errors:  _____

Number of Correct Words
Read Per Minute (WPM):  _____

Accuracy Rate:  _____

(Number of Correct Words Read per
Minute ÷ Total Words Read)

---

**READING FLUENCY**

|                    | Low | Average | High |
|--------------------|-----|---------|------|
| Decoding ability   | ○   | ○       | ○    |
| Pace               | ○   | ○       | ○    |
| Syntax             | ○   | ○       | ○    |
| Self-correction    | ○   | ○       | ○    |
| Intonation         | ○   | ○       | ○    |

**Record student rates on the Oral Fluency Scores pages.**

Name _____ Date _____ Score _____

# Benjamin Banneker, Pioneering Scientist

## Vocabulary

**Read each item. Fill in the bubble for the answer you think is correct.**

**1.** Which word best completes both sentences?

   **The restaurant added the _____ to our bill.**

   **The _____ of the paintbrush needs cleaning.**

   Ⓐ handle       Ⓒ check

   ⬤Ⓑ tip       Ⓓ tax

**2.** Another word for **skill** is

   Ⓐ job.       Ⓒ memory.

   Ⓑ secret.       ⬤Ⓓ ability.

**3.** Maryland was one of the thirteen American **colonies** ruled by Great Britain. **Colonies** are

   ⬤Ⓐ settlements.       Ⓒ plantations.

   Ⓑ large, wooden ships.       Ⓓ farmers' markets.

**4.** **Astronomy** is the study of

   Ⓐ American history.       Ⓒ growing crops.

   Ⓑ government.       ⬤Ⓓ the universe.

**5.** Helping survey the **capital** city was a great honor. The **capital** city is

   Ⓐ an area far away from any large city.

   Ⓑ a place near the shore.

   Ⓒ where the government is located.

   Ⓓ a forested area.

**Benjamin Banneker, Pioneering Scientist** (continued)

# Comprehension

**Read the following questions carefully. Then completely fill in the bubble of each correct answer. You may look back at the selection to find the answer to each of the questions.**

**1.** Why did young Benjamin Banneker count things?

Ⓐ It was part of his job on the farm.

Ⓑ It was important to keep track of the number of rows in a field.

Ⓒ It made his lonely work more fun.

Ⓓ It was practice for what he was learning at school.

**2.** Which of the following is an opinion?

Ⓐ Andrew Ellicott asked Banneker to help him survey the land.

Ⓑ Banneker quit school after only four years.

Ⓒ George Washington deserved to be the first president.

Ⓓ George Ellicott owned a telescope.

## Benjamin Banneker, Pioneering Scientist (continued)

3. Which of these jobs did Banneker not have?

   (A) writer

   (B) teacher

   (C) surveyor

   (D) farmer

4. At the end of the selection, Banneker

   (A) was still working on the farm.

   (B) was not a very old man.

   (C) was building a new clock.

   (D) was still asking questions.

5. Who taught Banneker to read?

   (A) his teacher in a one room schoolhouse

   (B) his grandmother Molly

   (C) his great grandfather

   (D) the plantation owner

**Benjamin Banneker, Pioneering Scientist** (continued)

**Read the following questions carefully. Use complete sentences to answer the questions.** Possible answers below

**6.** How were Banneker and his family different from most African Americans living in 1737?

They were no longer slaves; they owned a farm.

**7.** "Grandmother was teaching Benjamin to read. Benjamin was a fast learner." Identify each sentence from the selection as either a fact or opinion.

The first sentence is a fact, and the second sentence is an opinion.

**8.** Why did Banneker quit school after four years?

He was young and strong, and his family needed him on the farm.

**9.** How was Banneker different from the other farmers who lived nearby?

He could read and write; he told them what their crops were worth.

**10.** Why did Banneker send a copy of his almanac to Thomas Jefferson?

Jefferson was important; Banneker wanted to give him his opinions.

## Benjamin Banneker, Pioneering Scientist (continued)

Read the question below. Write complete sentences for your answer. Support your answer with information from the selection.

**Linking to the Concepts** How did Banneker become famous?

_____

_____

_____

_____

_____

Read the question below. Your answer should be based on your own experience. Write complete sentences for your answer.

**Personal Response** How does it make you feel to read about the accomplishments of a person such as Banneker? Explain the reasons behind your feelings.

_____

_____

_____

_____

_____

## Benjamin Banneker, Pioneering Scientist (continued)

## Grammar, Usage, and Mechanics

**Read each question. Fill in the bubble beside the answer in each group that is correct. If none of the answers is correct, choose the last answer, "none of the above."**

**1.** Which sentence contains a relative pronoun?

Ⓐ Cathy bought a mirror that was old.

Ⓑ Ian played with John and him.

Ⓒ She tried hard to win the game.

Ⓓ none of the above

**2.** Which sentence contains a relative pronoun?

Ⓐ His brother came to visit the school.

Ⓑ He could not sit still during class.

Ⓒ She saw people who had graduated.

Ⓓ none of the above

**3.** In which sentence is a demonstrative pronoun underlined?

Ⓐ <u>These</u> are great pencils.  Ⓒ These <u>are</u> great pencils.

Ⓑ These are <u>great</u> pencils.  Ⓓ none of the above

**4.** In which sentence is a demonstrative pronoun underlined?

Ⓐ I do <u>not</u> think his shoes go with that.

Ⓑ <u>I</u> do not think <u>his</u> shoes go with that.

Ⓒ I do not think his shoes go <u>with</u> that.

Ⓓ none of the above

**5.** Which sentence is correct?

Ⓐ Chris reads two *newspapers*.

Ⓑ I watched the movie Bambi.

Ⓒ My mother read *Oliver Twist*.

Ⓓ none of the above

## Benjamin Banneker, Pioneering Scientist (continued)

## Analyzing the Selection

**Read the question below. Write complete sentences for your answer. Support your answer with information from the selections.**

Imagine that you were Banneker's best friend. How would he influence you, and how would you influence him?

_____

_____

_____

_____

_____

_____

_____

_____

_____

_____

_____

_____

_____

_____

## Benjamin Banneker, Pioneering Scientist (continued)

## Oral Fluency Assessment

### *Mice Have Come a Long Way*

| | |
|---|---|
| Mice are good at pointing things out. Not the little furry | 1–11 |
| creatures, but the mice that help you use a computer. | 12–21 |
| As you probably know, a mouse helps you find things on | 22–32 |
| your computer screen. The mouse got its name from the fact | 33–43 |
| that the first mouse had a cord coming out the end. It looked | 44–56 |
| like a tail! | 57–59 |
| A man named Jay Smart invented that first computer mouse | 60–69 |
| in 1964. Smart's mouse was very different than mice you have | 70–80 |
| seen. It was a large cube. You would have had trouble getting | 81–92 |
| your hand around it! That blocky mouse had two big wheels | 93–103 |
| inside of it, too. | 104–107 |
| Mice were improved when it was found that a rolling | 108–117 |
| ball could take the place of the wheels. Today many mice | 118–128 |
| are wireless. They have lost their tails. This is because mice | 129–139 |
| no longer need a cord to connect to the computer. It seems | 140–151 |
| doubtful that mice will ever lose their names. That means we | 152–162 |
| can look forward to having these helpful critters next to our | 163–173 |
| computers for years to come. | 174–178 |

---

**EVALUATING CODES FOR ORAL FLUENCY**

sky       (/) words read incorrectly

blue
^  sky    (^) inserted word
         ( ] ) after the last word

---

**READING RATE AND ACCURACY**

Total Words Read:       _____

Number of Errors:     _____

Number of Correct Words
Read Per Minute (WPM):   _____

Accuracy Rate:      _____

(Number of Correct Words Read per
Minute ÷ Total Words Read)

---

**READING FLUENCY**

| | Low | Average | High |
|---|---|---|---|
| Decoding ability | ○ | ○ | ○ |
| Pace | ○ | ○ | ○ |
| Syntax | ○ | ○ | ○ |
| Self-correction | ○ | ○ | ○ |
| Intonation | ○ | ○ | ○ |

**Record student rates on the Oral Fluency Scores pages.**

Name _____  Date _____  Score _____

# Striking It Rich: The Story of the California Gold Rush

## Vocabulary

**Read each item. Fill in the bubble for the answer you think is correct.**

1. If something is **elegant,** it is

   (A) very large.
   (C) very colorful
   (B) imaginary.
   (D) of high quality.

2. Which word contains the Latin root meaning "to do"?

   (A) natural
   (C) formula
   (B) active
   (D) biology

3. There were plenty of **rumors** about gold in California. **Rumors** are

   (A) stories without proof.
   (B) special mining tools.
   (C) factories.
   (D) people without property.

4. Sutter was afraid that word of the gold could **distract** the men. In this sentence, **distract** means

   (A) help them do their jobs better.
   (B) make the men ill.
   (C) focus their attention on their jobs.
   (D) draw their attention away from their jobs.

5. The president spoke of the **abundance** of gold in California. An **abundance** is

   (A) a nugget.
   (C) a location.
   (B) a promise.
   (D) a large amount.

**Striking It Rich: The Story of the California Gold Rush** (continued)

## Comprehension

**Read the following questions carefully. Then completely fill in the bubble of each correct answer. You may look back at the selection to find the answer to each of the questions.**

1. Where was the gold near San Francisco first discovered?

   Ⓐ in a field

   Ⓑ in a river

   Ⓒ in a well

   Ⓓ in a canyon

2. How is gold similar to iron pyrite?

   Ⓐ Both flatten when hit with a hammer.

   Ⓑ Both weigh about the same.

   Ⓒ Both are glittering yellow rocks.

   Ⓓ Both become dim if dabbed with acid.

## Striking It Rich: The Story of the California Gold Rush (continued)

3. Which way to get to California turned out to be a failure at the time?

   Ⓐ going by train

   Ⓑ going by boat

   Ⓒ going by wagon

   Ⓓ going by air

4. Why were the miners called Forty-Niners?

   Ⓐ They went to California in 1849.

   Ⓑ There were forty-nine of them.

   Ⓒ It cost forty-nine dollars to get to California.

   Ⓓ It took forty-nine days to get to California.

5. Why did the author write the selection?

   Ⓐ to explain how to mine for gold

   Ⓑ to tell about an event in American history

   Ⓒ to tell about different ways of traveling

   Ⓓ to show how San Francisco became a major city

**Striking It Rich: The Story of the California Gold Rush** (continued)

**Read the following questions carefully. Use complete sentences to answer the questions.** Possible answers below

6. What happened soon after President Polk made a speech that mentioned the gold in California?

   Many people left their homes to look for gold in California.

7. How did most Easterners get to California?

   They went by boat around South America.

8. What did the author report about the route to California that involved crossing Panama?

   It took the least amount of time if things went well, which they rarely did.

9. Name two things that killed many people who were going to California by land.

   Many people died from cholera or due to accidents with guns.

10. Why did the miners think their troubles were over when they got to California?

    They had survived the journey and thought that they would become rich.

**Striking It Rich: The Story of the California Gold Rush** (continued)

**Read the question below. Write complete sentences for your answer. Support your answer with information from the selection.**

**Linking to the Concepts** How did the gold rush change the United States?

_____

_____

_____

_____

_____

**Read the question below. Your answer should be based on your own experience. Write complete sentences for your answer.**

**Personal Response** Do you think you would have been lured to California by the dream of gold? Explain your answer.

_____

_____

_____

_____

_____

_____

**Striking It Rich: The Story of the California Gold Rush** (continued)

## Grammar, Usage, and Mechanics

Read each question. Fill in the bubble beside the answer in each group that is correct. If none of the answers is correct, choose the last answer, "none of the above."

**1.** In which sentence is the adjective used correctly?

Ⓐ It is the more busier street.

Ⓑ It is the busiest street.

Ⓒ It is the most busiest street.

Ⓓ none of the above

**2.** What is the best way to combine these sentences?
**Debbie's dog is brown. Debbie's dog is big.**

Ⓐ Debbie's dog is brown; and her dog is big.

Ⓑ Debbie's dog is brown, Debbie's dog is big.

Ⓒ Debbie's dog is big and brown.

Ⓓ none of the above

**3.** In which sentence is the subject underlined?

Ⓐ Paula's aunt knits <u>mittens</u>.

Ⓑ The <u>first</u> mittens were too big.

Ⓒ She gave <u>those</u> to her older sister.

Ⓓ none of the above

**4.** In which sentence is the verb underlined?

Ⓐ Angela <u>learned</u> to skate on the pond.

Ⓑ Now she takes ice <u>skating</u> lessons.

Ⓒ <u>Soon</u> she will skate in an ice show.

Ⓓ none of the above

**5.** What is the correct way to begin a paragraph?

Ⓐ with an adjective

Ⓑ with a verb

Ⓒ with an indent

Ⓓ none of the above

**Striking It Rich: The Story of the California Gold Rush** (continued)

## Analyzing the Selection

**Read the question below. Write complete sentences for your answer. Support your answer with information from the selections.**

Based on the first three selections in this unit, what are some conclusions you can draw about the early years of the United States?

_____

_____

_____

_____

_____

_____

_____

_____

_____

_____

_____

_____

_____

## Striking It Rich: The Story of the California Gold Rush (continued)

## Oral Fluency Assessment

### *The Polar Bear*

It is white, eleven feet tall, and weighs nearly a thousand      1–11
pounds. It is an excellent swimmer. It can smell something      12–21
twenty miles away. What is it? It is a polar bear.      22–32

These huge beasts live on the icy land near the North Pole.      33–44
Their fur blends in with the snow to make them nearly invisible.      45–56
Only their black noses stand out. When a polar bear is hunting,      57–68
it will cover its nose with a paw to better hide itself      69–80

A polar bear uses its front legs to swim, and it can swim at      81–94
about six miles per hour. These bears sometimes swim fifty      95–104
miles from the nearest ice or land. When they swim, they open      105–116
their eyes and close their noses. They can stay under for two      117–128
minutes. As soon as they get out of the cold water, they shake      129–141
themselves. This keeps the water from freezing in their fur.      142–151

At one time the number of polar bears was down to about      152–163
five thousand. Strict hunting rules have helped to increase their      164–173
number. More than forty thousand bears now live in the      174–183
Arctic regions.      184–185

---

**EVALUATING CODES
FOR ORAL FLUENCY**

sky          (/) words read incorrectly

blue
 ^  sky      (^) inserted word
             ( ] ) after the last word

---

**READING RATE AND ACCURACY**

Total Words Read:      _____

Number of Errors:      _____

Number of Correct Words
Read Per Minute (WPM):      _____

Accuracy Rate:      _____

(Number of Correct Words Read per
Minute ÷ Total Words Read)

---

**READING FLUENCY**

| | Low | Average | High |
|---|---|---|---|
| Decoding ability | ○ | ○ | ○ |
| Pace | ○ | ○ | ○ |
| Syntax | ○ | ○ | ○ |
| Self-correction | ○ | ○ | ○ |
| Intonation | ○ | ○ | ○ |

---

Record student rates on the Oral Fluency Scores pages.

Name _____ Date _____ Score _____

# A Covered Wagon Girl

## Vocabulary

**Read each item. Fill in the bubble for the answer you think is correct.**

1. Which Greek root means "to write"?

   Ⓐ *graph*          Ⓒ *photo*

   Ⓑ *meter*          Ⓓ *tele*

2. Another word for **vast** is

   Ⓐ silly.           Ⓒ bright.

   Ⓑ sleepy.          Ⓓ large.

3. The group descended a **tremendous** hill at Bear Valley. **Tremendous** means about the same as

   Ⓐ very large.

   Ⓑ steep.

   Ⓒ beautiful.

   Ⓓ jagged.

4. Sallie's father goes to Sacramento to get **provisions**. **Provisions** are

   Ⓐ fancy clothing.

   Ⓑ supplies.

   Ⓒ cattle.

   Ⓓ people to help build a church.

5. They are looking for a **permanent** home. **Permanent** means

   Ⓐ large.           Ⓒ rural.

   Ⓑ urban.           Ⓓ lasting.

**A Covered Wagon Girl** (continued)

## Comprehension

**Read the following questions carefully. Then completely fill in the bubble of each correct answer. You may look back at the selection to find the answer to each of the questions.**

**1.** Which of these is a fact from the selection?

   Ⓐ The roads were terrible.

   Ⓑ The boat traveled on the Missouri River.

   Ⓒ The stream seemed angry.

   Ⓓ The springs were a beautiful sight.

**2.** Where does the selection begin?

   Ⓐ Nebraska

   Ⓑ Idaho

   Ⓒ Indiana

   Ⓓ Missouri

**A Covered Wagon Girl** (continued)

**3.** Which of these was NOT a way the author traveled?

Ⓐ by canoe

Ⓑ on foot

Ⓒ by steamboat

Ⓓ by carriage

**4.** At the end of the selection, the author will

Ⓐ go live in San Jose.

Ⓑ travel east in search of a job.

Ⓒ be hired to take more settlers to California.

Ⓓ leave for the West on a boat.

**5.** The author wrote this selection in order to

Ⓐ inform other people about the dangers of a wagon train trip.

Ⓑ show other people what they would need for a similar trip.

Ⓒ tell about some of the beautiful sights of the West.

Ⓓ have a personal record of the trip.

**A Covered Wagon Girl** (continued)

**Read the following questions carefully. Use complete sentences to answer the questions.** Possible answers below

6. How is Fort Laramie like a small town?

   Fort Laramie had all types of business activities happening.

7. Why does the group spend the winter in Fremont?

   They stay there because the rainy season is coming, and they are tired.

8. What point of view is featured in this selection?

   It is a diary written in the first-person point of view.

9. Why did the group stop on Sundays?

   They were religious people and Sunday was a day of rest.

10. Why did the group get held up at Devil's Gate?

   Some children had wandered off and a search party had to be formed.

**A Covered Wagon Girl** (continued)

**Read the question below. Write complete sentences for your answer. Support your answer with information from the selection.**

**Linking to the Concepts** Why was the group in this selection going to California?

_____

_____

_____

_____

_____

**Read the prompt below. Your answer should be based on your own experience. Write complete sentences for your answer.**

**Personal Response** Have you ever taken a long trip? Write a journal entry about something that happened on the trip.

_____

_____

_____

_____

_____

**A Covered Wagon Girl** (continued)

# Grammar, Usage, and Mechanics

**Read each question. Fill in the bubble beside the answer in each group that is correct.**

**1.** In which sentence is the adjective used correctly?

Ⓐ This cat is more larger.   Ⓒ This cat is most largest.

Ⓑ This cat is larger.   Ⓓ none of the above

**2.** What is the best way to combine these sentences?
**A pretty butterfly landed. The butterfly was yellow.**

Ⓐ A pretty butterfly landed, and it was yellow.

Ⓑ A pretty butterfly landed, the butterfly was yellow.

Ⓒ A pretty yellow butterfly landed.

Ⓓ none of the above

**3.** In which sentence is the adjective used incorrectly?

Ⓐ I think Alonzo is taller than Pedro.

Ⓑ This skyscraper is the taller of those two buildings.

Ⓒ That ladder is the more tallest one of all.

Ⓓ none of the above

**4.** What is the best way to combine these sentences?
**The water in the river was cold. It was also clear.**

Ⓐ The water in the river was cold, but it was also clear.

Ⓑ The water in the river was cold and it was also clear.

Ⓒ The water in the river was cold: so it was also clear.

Ⓓ none of the above

**5.** In which sentence are the parentheses used correctly?

Ⓐ The name of the hero is Zeb (short for zebra).

Ⓑ Paul jumped higher than anyone (including me.)

Ⓒ The prizes went to (two girls Mary and Anna.)

Ⓓ none of the above

**A Covered Wagon Girl** (continued)

## Analyzing the Selection

**Read the question below. Write complete sentences for your answer. Support your answer with information from the selection.**

Think about "The Diary of Sallie Hester." Which entries helped you understand the journey best? Summarize these entries and explain why you chose them.

_____

_____

_____

_____

_____

_____

_____

_____

_____

_____

_____

_____

_____

## A Covered Wagon Girl (continued)

# Oral Fluency Assessment

### *Uncle Bob Surprises Jane*

| | |
|---|---|
| Almost every Saturday morning, Uncle Bob stopped by | 1–8 |
| Jane's house and took her on a trip. Uncle Bob was her mother's | 9–21 |
| brother. He was also her father's best friend. Jane had to admit | 22–33 |
| that Uncle Bob was her "best uncle," if such a term existed. | 34–45 |
| On this Saturday morning, Uncle Bob said he had a surprise. | 46–56 |
| Instead of getting in the car, they walked to the subway. They | 57–68 |
| got on the next train that came by. After a short ride, they got | 69–82 |
| off the train. Jane had never gotten off at that stop before. | 83–94 |
| They walked up the stairs to the exit. Then Jane saw her | 95–106 |
| surprise. They were in front of a building with huge columns | 107–117 |
| holding up the roof. | 118–121 |
| "This is the Museum of Natural History, Jane. It has some of | 122–133 |
| the neatest things you will ever see. I thought you might like | 134–145 |
| spending the day here." | 146–149 |
| Jane was speechless as they walked up the steps and through | 150–160 |
| the doors. There, in the middle of a huge hallway was a dinosaur | 161–173 |
| skeleton! Jane loved science. She was sure this was going to be | 174–185 |
| one of the best mornings ever with "best uncle" Bob. | 186–195 |

---

**EVALUATING CODES FOR ORAL FLUENCY**

sky  (/) words read incorrectly

blue
^  sky  (^) inserted word
      ( ] ) after the last word

---

**READING RATE AND ACCURACY**

Total Words Read: _____

Number of Errors: _____

Number of Correct Words
Read Per Minute (WPM): _____

Accuracy Rate: _____

(Number of Correct Words Read per
Minute ÷ Total Words Read)

---

**READING FLUENCY**

| | Low | Average | High |
|---|---|---|---|
| Decoding ability | ◯ | ◯ | ◯ |
| Pace | ◯ | ◯ | ◯ |
| Syntax | ◯ | ◯ | ◯ |
| Self-correction | ◯ | ◯ | ◯ |
| Intonation | ◯ | ◯ | ◯ |

**Record student rates on the Oral Fluency Scores pages.**

Name _____ Date _____ Score _____

# Abraham Lincoln: Sixteenth President

## Vocabulary

**Read each item. Fill in the bubble for the answer you think is correct.**

**1.** What is the correct contraction of *will not*?

   Ⓐ will'no       Ⓒ willn't

   Ⓑ won't        Ⓓ w'not

**2.** A **legislator** is a

   Ⓐ state governor.     Ⓒ shopkeeper.

   Ⓑ police officer.     Ⓓ lawmaker.

**3.** Abe enjoyed **politics** a lot. **Politics** is the study of

   Ⓐ farming.        Ⓒ the government.

   Ⓑ running a store.    Ⓓ law.

**4.** Many Americans were impressed with Lincoln's **intelligence. Intelligence** is

   Ⓐ height.

   Ⓑ strength.

   Ⓒ ability to think and understand.

   Ⓓ basic family values.

**5.** The United States is a nation conceived in **liberty.** This means that our citizens have

   Ⓐ freedom to act, think, or speak as they please.

   Ⓑ very many responsibilities.

   Ⓒ a need to speak up for themselves.

   Ⓓ the right to vote.

**Abraham Lincoln: Sixteenth President** (continued)

## Comprehension

**Read the following questions carefully. Then completely fill in the bubble of each correct answer. You may look back at the selection to find the answer to each of the questions.**

**1.** Why did Lincoln's father keep moving the family?

Ⓐ He was worried about a sickness in the area.

Ⓑ He was looking for better educational opportunities for his children.

Ⓒ He was looking for better farmland.

Ⓓ He was in the military.

**2.** All of these are mentioned as young Lincoln's favorite reading material EXCEPT

Ⓐ *Oliver Twist.*

Ⓑ *Aesop's Fables.*

Ⓒ *Robinson Crusoe.*

Ⓓ the plays of William Shakespeare.

## Abraham Lincoln: Sixteenth President (continued)

**3.** Which of these happened to Lincoln after he became a state legislator?

Ⓐ  His mother died.

Ⓑ  His managed a general store in New Salem.

Ⓒ  He helped his father build log cabins.

Ⓓ  He met Mary Todd.

**4.** What event started the Civil War?

Ⓐ  the battle of Bull Run

Ⓑ  the firing on Fort Sumter

Ⓒ  the debates between Lincoln and Douglas

Ⓓ  the Gettysburg Address

**5.** President Lincoln died

Ⓐ  before the Civil War ended.

Ⓑ  right before the battle of Bull Run.

Ⓒ  after the slaves were freed.

Ⓓ  before the Thirteenth Amendment was passed.

**Abraham Lincoln: Sixteenth President** (continued)

Read the following questions carefully. Use complete sentences to answer the questions. Possible answers below

6. How was the country divided during Lincoln's presidency?

The southern states seceded and said they were a separate country.

7. What was the debate about slavery in the new territories?

Many thought slavery was wrong and did not want it in the new territories.

8. Why did the people in New Salem enjoy Lincoln's company?

They thought he was a great storyteller and told good jokes.

9. Put these events in the proper sequence: Lincoln marries Mary Todd, Lincoln passes law exam, Lincoln debates Douglas.

Lincoln passes law exam, marries Mary Todd, debates Douglas.

10. Why did the South win some of the early battles of the Civil War?

The South won these battles because of its great generals.

## Abraham Lincoln: Sixteenth President (continued)

Read the question below. Write complete sentences for your answer. Support your answer with information from the selection.

**Linking to the Concepts** Why do people remember Lincoln fondly?

_____

_____

_____

_____

_____

Read the question below. Your answer should be based on your own experience. Write complete sentences for your answer.

**Personal Response** Some people think that Lincoln was the greatest president. What is your opinion? Explain why you think this way.

_____

_____

_____

_____

_____

## Abraham Lincoln: Sixteenth President (continued)

# Grammar, Usage, and Mechanics

**Read each question. Fill in the bubble beside the answer in each group that is correct. If none of the answers is correct, choose the last answer, "none of the above."**

**1.** Which sentence contains an adverb?

Ⓐ Axel jumped over the fence quickly.

Ⓑ Jamaica's new hairstyle was beautiful.

Ⓒ Three people worked at the railway station.

Ⓓ none of the above

**2.** In which sentence is the adverb used correctly?

Ⓐ Jada walked more quicklier.    Ⓒ Jada walked quickly.

Ⓑ Jada walked quicklier.    Ⓓ none of the above

**3.** In which sentence is the adverb used correctly?

Ⓐ Min plays better than anyone on the team.

Ⓑ Min plays more better than anyone on the team.

Ⓒ Min plays gooder than anyone on the team.

Ⓓ none of the above

**4.** In which sentence is the adverb used incorrectly?

Ⓐ Nia danced beautifully on the stage.

Ⓑ Lennie answered the questions properly.

Ⓒ That road curves dangerously.

Ⓓ none of the above

**5.** In which sentence is the adverb used incorrectly?

Ⓐ Be sure to close the door more tighter.

Ⓑ The moon is shining more brightly than before.

Ⓒ The ice was melting rapidly.

Ⓓ none of the above

## Abraham Lincoln: Sixteenth President (continued)

## Analyzing the Selection

**Read the question below. Write complete sentences for your answer. Support your answer with information from the selections.**

You read about three individuals in this unit, Benjamin Banneker, Sallie Hester, and Abraham Lincoln. How did they each contribute in their own way to the development of the United States?

_____

_____

_____

_____

_____

_____

_____

_____

_____

_____

_____

## Abraham Lincoln: Sixteenth President (continued)

## Oral Fluency Assessment

### *Mike the Hero*

| | |
|---|---|
| The building was on fire! Mike knew that the only way to | 1–12 |
| escape was to climb out the window and get to the fire escape. | 13–25 |
| He heard his brother, Pat, cry out in his sleep. He heard his | 26–38 |
| father's voice saying, "The fire is in the hall, and I can't reach | 39–51 |
| the children!" | 52–53 |

| | |
|---|---|
| Mike knew what he had to do. He grabbed some blankets | 54–64 |
| and wrapped Pat in them. Pat started to cry, so Mike talked to | 65–77 |
| him and told him not to be scared. He carefully climbed out of | 78–90 |
| the burning building and made his way over to the fire escape | 91–102 |
| with the heavy child in his arms. | 103–109 |

| | |
|---|---|
| When they reached the ground, people were crying and | 110–118 |
| screaming. Mike handed his brother to a firefighter and sat | 119–128 |
| down on the ground. He felt very alone and very afraid. Just | 129–140 |
| then his mother and father rushed up to the boys and hugged | 141–152 |
| them both. "When I couldn't make it down the hall I thought . . ." | 153–164 |
| Mike's father trailed off. | 165–168 |

| | |
|---|---|
| "Michael," his mother said, "you are a hero for saving your | 169–179 |
| brother's life." | 180–181 |

---

**EVALUATING CODES
FOR ORAL FLUENCY**

sky      (/) words read incorrectly

blue
^  sky   (^) inserted word
           ( ] ) after the last word

---

**READING RATE AND ACCURACY**

Total Words Read:  _____

Number of Errors:  _____

Number of Correct Words
Read Per Minute (WPM):  _____

Accuracy Rate:  _____

(Number of Correct Words Read per
Minute ÷ Total Words Read)

---

**READING FLUENCY**

| | Low | Average | High |
|---|---|---|---|
| Decoding ability | ○ | ○ | ○ |
| Pace | ○ | ○ | ○ |
| Syntax | ○ | ○ | ○ |
| Self-correction | ○ | ○ | ○ |
| Intonation | ○ | ○ | ○ |

---

**Record student rates on the Oral Fluency Scores pages.**

**Name** _____ **Date** _____ **Score** _____

# Persuasive Writing

## Writing Situation
The most interesting character in American history

## Audience
Your classmates

## Directions for Writing
The history of America includes many interesting people. Write about the person in American history who you think is most interesting. Explain what makes this person so interesting to you. Write in a way that will make the character seem interesting to your readers.

## Checklist
You will earn the best score if you
- think about your person and plan your writing before you begin.
- have a beginning paragraph that gets the attention of readers.
- vary your sentences and the words you use.
- make the person you chose seem interesting to readers.
- give many interesting details about the person.
- write more sentences and longer sentences when you revise.
- use correct capital letters, punctuation, and spelling.
- use subjects, verbs, and modifiers correctly.
- choose words that mean what you want to say.
- write complete sentences and avoid fragments or run-ons.

# Four Point Rubrics for Persuasive Writing

| Genre | 1 Point | 2 Points | 3 Points | 4 Points |
|---|---|---|---|---|
| Persuasive | Position is absent or confusing. Insufficient writing to show that criteria are met. | Position is vague or lacks clarity. Unrelated ideas or multiple positions are included. | An opening statement identifies position. Writing may develop few or more points than delineated in opening. Focus may be too broad. | Sets scope and purpose of paper in introduction. Maintains position throughout. Supports arguments. Includes effective closing. |
| **Writing Traits** | | | | |
| Audience | Displays little or no sense of audience. Does not engage audience. | Displays some sense of audience. | Writes with audience in mind throughout. | Displays a strong sense of audience. Engages audience. |
| Focus | Topic is unclear or wanders and must be inferred. Extraneous material may be present. | Topic/position/direction is unclear and must be inferred. | Topic/position is stated and direction/ purpose is previewed and maintained. Mainly stays on topic. | Topic/position is clearly stated, previewed, and maintained throughout the paper. Topics and details are tied together with a central theme or purpose that is maintained /threaded throughout the paper. |
| Organization | The writing lacks coherence; organization seems haphazard and disjointed. Plan is not evident. Facts are presented randomly. No transitions are included. Beginning is weak and ending is abrupt. There is no awareness of paragraph structure or organization. | An attempt has been made to organize the writing; however, the overall structure is inconsistent or skeletal. Plan is evident but loosely structured or writer overuses a particular pattern. Writing may be a listing of facts/ideas with a weak beginning or conclusion. Transitions are awkward or nonexistent. Includes beginning use of paragraphs. | Organization is clear and coherent. Order and structure are present, but may seem formulaic. Plan is evident. Reasons for order of key concepts may be unclear. Beginning or conclusion is included but may lack impact. Transitions are present. Paragraph use is appropriate. | The organization enhances the central idea and its development. The order and structure are compelling and move the reader through the text easily. Plan is evident. Key concepts are logically sequenced. Beginning grabs attention. Conclusion adds impact. Uses a variety of transitions that enhance meaning. Uses paragraphs appropriately. |
| **Writing Conventions** | | | | |
| Conventions Overall | Numerous errors in usage, grammar, spelling, capitalization, and punctuation repeatedly distract the reader and make the text difficult to read. The reader finds it difficult to focus on the message. | The writing demonstrates limited control of standard writing conventions (punctuation, spelling, capitalization, grammar, and usage). Errors sometimes impede readability. | The writing demonstrates control of standard writing conventions (punctuation, spelling, capitalization, grammar, and usage). Minor errors, while perhaps noticeable, do not impede readability. | The writing demonstrates exceptionally strong control of standard writing conventions (punctuation, spelling, capitalization, grammar, and usage) and uses them effectively to enhance communication. Errors are so few and so minor that the reader can easily skim over them. |

# Six Point Rubrics

Use the following rubrics to assess student writing.

## 6 Points

The writing is focused, purposeful, and reflects insight into the writing situation. The paper conveys a sense of completeness and wholeness with adherence to the main idea, and its organizational pattern provides for a logical progression of ideas. The support is substantial, specific, relevant, concrete, and/or illustrative. The paper demonstrates a commitment to and an involvement with the subject, clarity in presentation of ideas, and may use creative writing strategies appropriate to the purpose of the paper. The writing demonstrates a mature command of language (word choice) with freshness of expression. Sentence structure is varied, and sentences are complete except when fragments are used purposefully. Few, if any, convention errors occur in mechanics, usage, and punctuation.

## 5 Points

The writing focuses on the topic, and its organizational pattern provides for a progression of ideas, although some lapses may occur. The paper conveys a sense of completeness or wholeness. The support is ample. The writing demonstrates a mature command of language, including precise word choice. There is variation in sentence structure, and, with rare exceptions, sentences are complete except when fragments are used purposefully. The paper generally follows the conventions of mechanics, usage, and spelling.

## 4 Points

The writing is generally focused on the topic but may include extraneous or loosely related material. An organizational pattern is apparent, although some lapses may occur. The paper exhibits some sense of completeness or wholeness. The support, including word choice, is adequate, although development may be uneven. There is little variation in sentence structure, and most sentences are complete. The paper generally follows the conventions of mechanics, usage, and spelling.

## 3 Points

The writing is generally focused on the topic but may include extraneous or loosely related material. An organizational pattern has been attempted, but the paper may lack a sense of completeness or wholeness. Some support is included, but developemt is erratic. Word choice is adequate but may be limited, predictable, or occasionally vague. There is little, if any, variation in sentence structure. Knowledge of the conventions of mechanics and usage is usually demonstrated, and commonly used words are usually spelled correctly.

## 2 Points

The writing is related to the topic but includes extraneous or loosely related material. Little evidence of an organizational pattern may be demonstrated, and the paper may lack a sense of completeness or wholeness. Development of support is inadequate or illogical. Word choice is limited, inappropriate, or vague. There is little, if any, variation in sentence structure, and gross errors in sentence structure may occur. Errors in basic conventions of mechanics and usage may occur, and commonly used words may be misspelled.

## 1 Point

The writing may only minimally address the topic. The paper is fragmentary or incoherent listing of related ideas or sentences or both. Little, if any, development of support or an organizational pattern or both is apparent. Limited or inappropriate word choice may obscure meaning. Gross errors in sentence structure and usage may impede communication. Frequent and blatant errors may occur in the basic conventions of mechanics and usage, and commonly used words may be misspelled.

## Unscorable

The paper is unscorable because

- the response is not related to what the prompt requested the student to do.
- the response is simply a rewording of the prompt
- the response is a copy of a published work.
- the student refused to write.
- the response is illegible.

- the response is incomprehensible (words are arrange in such a way that no meaning is conveyed).
- the response contains an insufficient amount of writing to determine if the student was attempting to address the prompt.

## Oral Fluency Scores

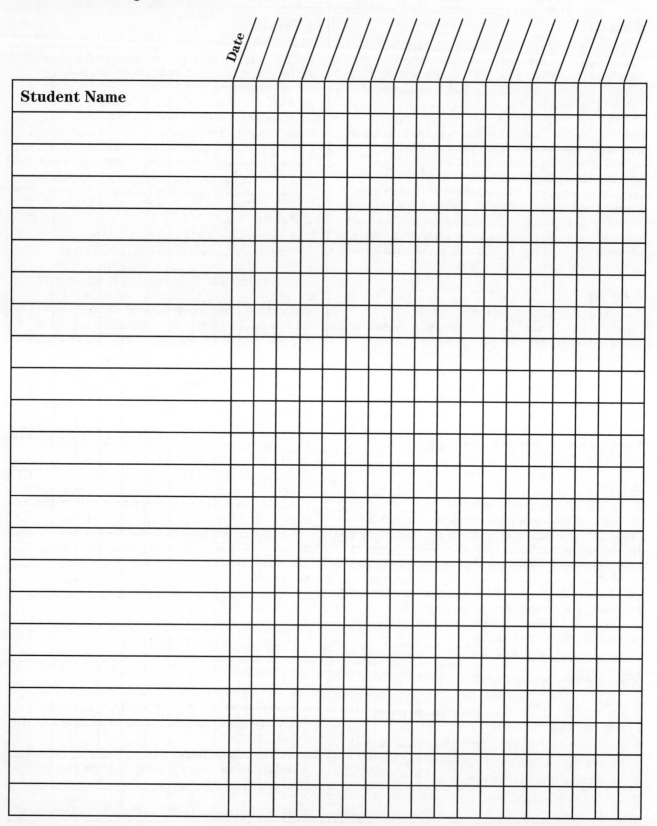

## Oral Fluency Scores

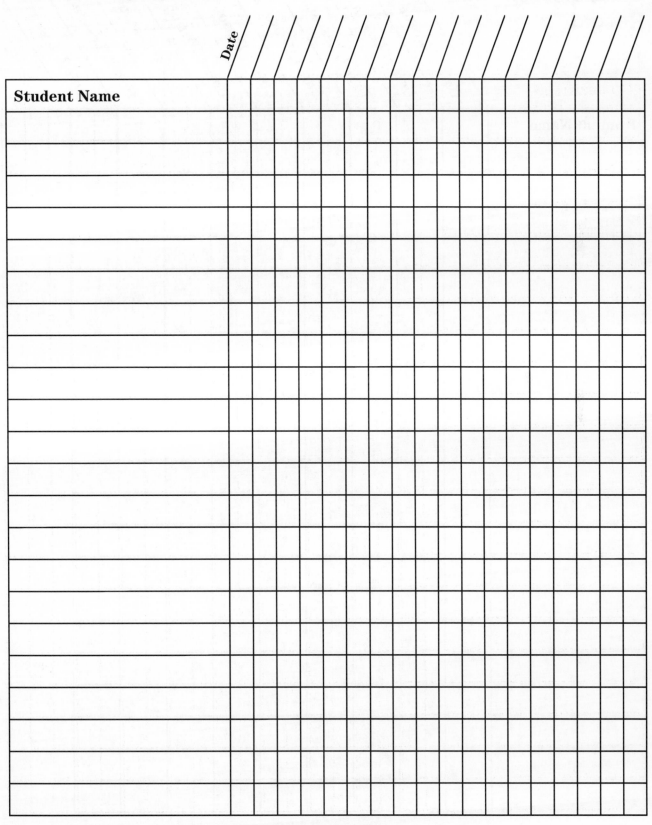

## Class Assessment Record

| Student Name | Unit 1, Lesson 1 | Unit 1, Lesson 2 | Unit 1, Lesson 3 | Unit 1, Lesson 4 | Unit 1, Lesson 5 | Unit 1 Writing Prompt | Unit 2, Lesson 1 | Unit 2, Lesson 2 | Unit 2, Lesson 3 |
|---|---|---|---|---|---|---|---|---|---|
| | | | | | | | | | |
| | | | | | | | | | |
| | | | | | | | | | |
| | | | | | | | | | |
| | | | | | | | | | |
| | | | | | | | | | |
| | | | | | | | | | |
| | | | | | | | | | |
| | | | | | | | | | |
| | | | | | | | | | |
| | | | | | | | | | |
| | | | | | | | | | |
| | | | | | | | | | |
| | | | | | | | | | |
| | | | | | | | | | |
| | | | | | | | | | |
| | | | | | | | | | |
| | | | | | | | | | |
| | | | | | | | | | |
| | | | | | | | | | |

## Class Assessment Record

| Student Name | Unit 2, Lesson 4 | Unit 2, Lesson 5 | Unit 2 Writing Prompt | Unit 3, Lesson 1 | Unit 3, Lesson 2 | Unit 3, Lesson 3 | Unit 3, Lesson 4 | Unit 3, Lesson 5 | Unit 3 Writing Prompt |
|---|---|---|---|---|---|---|---|---|---|
| | | | | | | | | | |
| | | | | | | | | | |
| | | | | | | | | | |
| | | | | | | | | | |
| | | | | | | | | | |
| | | | | | | | | | |
| | | | | | | | | | |
| | | | | | | | | | |
| | | | | | | | | | |
| | | | | | | | | | |
| | | | | | | | | | |
| | | | | | | | | | |
| | | | | | | | | | |
| | | | | | | | | | |
| | | | | | | | | | |
| | | | | | | | | | |
| | | | | | | | | | |
| | | | | | | | | | |
| | | | | | | | | | |
| | | | | | | | | | |

# Student Assessment Record

Name _____

Teacher _____ Grade _____

| Unit/ Lesson | Assessment Section | Date | Number Possible | Number Right | % | Score (Rubrics/WPM) |
|---|---|---|---|---|---|---|
|  |  |  |  |  |  |  |
|  |  |  |  |  |  |  |
|  |  |  |  |  |  |  |
|  |  |  |  |  |  |  |
|  |  |  |  |  |  |  |
|  |  |  |  |  |  |  |
|  |  |  |  |  |  |  |
|  |  |  |  |  |  |  |
|  |  |  |  |  |  |  |
|  |  |  |  |  |  |  |
|  |  |  |  |  |  |  |
|  |  |  |  |  |  |  |
|  |  |  |  |  |  |  |
|  |  |  |  |  |  |  |
|  |  |  |  |  |  |  |
|  |  |  |  |  |  |  |
|  |  |  |  |  |  |  |
|  |  |  |  |  |  |  |
|  |  |  |  |  |  |  |
|  |  |  |  |  |  |  |

# Comprehension Observation Log

**Student** _____ **Date** _____

**Unit** _____ **Lesson** _____ **Selection Title** _____

## General Comprehension
Concepts discussed: _____
_____

## Behavior Within a Group
Articulates, expresses ideas: _____
_____

Joins discussions: _____
_____

Collaborates (such as *works well with other students, works alone*): _____
_____

## Role in Group
Role (such as *leader, summarizer, questioner, critic, observer, non-participant*): _____
_____

Flexibility (changes roles when necessary): _____
_____

## Use of Reading Strategies
Uses strategies when needed (either those taught or student's choice of strategy)/Describes strategies used:
_____
_____
_____

Changes strategies when appropriate: _____
_____

---

**Changes Since Last Observation**

_____
_____
_____

---